LAB MANUAL

Glencoe Science

Biology

TEACHER EDITION

Biology Online
glencoe.com

Mc Graw Hill Glencoe

New York, New York   Columbus, Ohio   Chicago, Illinois   Peoria, Illinois   Woodland Hills, California

Glencoe

The **McGraw·Hill** Companies

Send all inquiries to:
Glencoe/McGraw-Hill
8787 Orion Place
Columbus, OH 43240-4027

ISBN-13: 978-0-07-874721-2
ISBN-10: 0-07-874721-X

Printed in the United States of America

2 3 4 5 6 7 8 9 10 11 045 11 10 09 08 07

Table of Contents

To the Teacher

This laboratory manual reinforces the concepts presented in all Glencoe biology texts. In the Teacher Edition, the chapters of each textbook corresponding to each laboratory activity are listed on pp. T5–T6. The activities in the manual, however, are designed to be used with any high school biology text.

The labs develop students' scientific literacy, scientific principles, and scientific inquiry. Students will increase their science vocabulary, learn how to handle laboratory equipment, use modern laboratory techniques, and acquire skill in working with tables and graphs. Scientific methods are important as students perform each activity, collect and record data, and form conclusions based on analysis and interpretation of experimental results. Students will utilize skills to carefully observe experimental procedures, accurately collect data, and graph and interpret results.

The Teacher Edition provides general information designed to aid you in the laboratory. Helpful teaching strategies and safety and disposal guidelines are outlined. Instructions for working with animals, cooperative learning, alternatives to dissection, a lab-by-lab materials list, and instructions for the preparation of solutions have been included to aid you in preparing for laboratory activities. Also included are models to be used with four activities.

The Teacher Edition provides a variety of helpful information about each activity in the *Teacher Guide and Answers* section. Teaching tips, helpful comments and suggestions, objectives, process skills, and time allotments, as well as possible answers to questions posed in the student edition, can be found in this section.

Correlation to Glencoe Biology Programs

The labs coordinate with the following chapters in these **Glencoe Biology** programs. Use this chart to help plan the best way to use these labs with your classes.

Lab	Glencoe Biology '07	BSCS Biology: A Molecular Approach	Biology: An Everyday Experience	Biology: Living Systems	Glencoe Living Environment
Lab 1: What makes mold grow?	Chapter 1	Prologue	Chapter 1	Chapter 2	Chapter 1
Lab 2: How does your biome grow?	Chapter 2	Chapter 2 and Chapter 24	Chapter 31	Chapter 29	Chapter 2
Lab 3: Do freshwater biomes respond differently to acid rain?	Chapter 3	Chapter 25	Chapter 32	Chapter 30	Chapter 3
Lab 4: How can you show a population trend?	Chapter 4	Chapter 25	Chapter 30	Chapter 27	Chapter 4
Lab 5: How do we measure biodiversity?	Chapter 5			Chapter 14	Chapter 5
Lab 6: How much vitamin C are you getting?	Chapter 6	Chapter 1	Chapter 9	Chapter 20	Chapter 6
Lab 7: What substances or solutions act as buffers?	Chapter 6	Chapter 2	Chapter 32	Chapter 3	Chapter 6
Lab 8: Why do cells divide?	Chapter 7	Chapter 8	Chapter 2	Chapter 7	Chapter 7
Lab 9: How many calories do foods contain?	Chapter 8	Chapter 2	Chapter 9	Chapter 3	Chapter 8
Lab 10: What can affect the rate of photosynthesis?	Chapter 8	Chapter 4	Chapter 19	Chapter 6	Chapter 8
Lab 11: How long does each phase of the cell cycle last?	Chapter 9	Chapter 8	Chapter 2	Chapter 7	Chapter 9
Lab 12: Green or yellow?	Chapter 10	Chapter 13	Chapter 26	Chapter 8	Chapter 10
Lab 13: What are the chances?	Chapter 11	Chapter 15	Chapter 27	Chapter 8	Chapter 11
Lab 14: What is DNA?	Chapter 12	Chapter 1	Chapter 28	Chapter 9	Chapter 12
Lab 15: Who did it?	Chapter 13	Chapter 15	Chapter 28	Chapter 9	Chapter 13
Lab 16: How do species compare?	Chapter 14	Chapter 19	Chapter 29	Chapter 14	Chapter 14
Lab 17: Could you beat natural selection?	Chapter 15	Prologue	Chapter 29	Chapter 13	Chapter 15
Lab 18: Does this animal walk on four legs or two?	Chapter 16	Chapter 20	Chapter 29	Chapter 13	Chapter 16
Lab 19: What is a taxonomic key?	Chapter 17	Chapter 18	Chapter 3	Chapter 14	Chapter 17
Lab 20: Can you filter out cholera?	Chapter 18	Chapter 15	Chapter 4	Chapter 15	Chapter 23
Lab 21: Do protists have good table manners?	Chapter 19	Chapter 18	Chapter 5	Chapter 15	Chapter 17, Chapter 21
Lab 22: What are mushroom spores?	Chapter 20	Chapter 18	Chapter 5	Chapter 15	Chapter 17, Chapter 22

Lab	Glencoe Biology '07	BSCS Biology: A Molecular Approach	Biology: An Everyday Experience	Biology: Living Systems	Glencoe Living Environment
Lab 23: How do ferns, mosses, and conifers reproduce?	Chapter 21	Chapter 18	Chapter 6	Chapter 16	Chapter 17, Chapter 22
Lab 24: Do plants sweat?	Chapter 22	Chapter 24	Chapter 19	Chapter 16, Chapter 21	Chapter 8, Chapter 17, Chapter 18
Lab 25: How does a flower grow?	Chapter 23	Chapter 12	Chapter 23	Chapter 18	Chapter 17, Chapter 22
Lab 26: Is that symmetrical?	Chapter 24	Chapter 10	Chapter 7	Chapter 17	Student Resources
Lab 27: Which will the worm choose?	Chapter 25	Chapter 22	Chapter 7	Chapter 28	Chapter 17, Chapter 19
Lab 28: What is living in the leaf litter?	Chapter 26	Chapter 18	Chapter 31	Chapter 28	Chapter 17
Lab 29: How can you analyze echinoderm relationships?	Chapter 27	Chapter 18	Chapter 7	Chapter 17	Chapter 17
Lab 30: How have frogs adapted to terrestrial and aquatic habitats?	Chapter 28	Chapter 10	Chapter 29	Chapter 17	Chapter 17
Lab 31: What are the structures and functions of a chicken egg?	Chapter 29	Chapter 19	Chapter 29	Chapter 17	Chapter 22
Lab 32: What is the best way to keep warm?	Chapter 30	Chapter 5	Chapter 8	Chapter 17	Chapter 18
Lab 33: How do we learn?	Chapter 31	Chapter 21	Chapter 17	Chapter 19	Chapter 19
Lab 34: How long can you last?	Chapter 32	Chapter 7	Chapter 14	Chapter 26	Chapter 18
Lab 35: How quickly do you respond?	Chapter 33	Chapter 21	Chapter 15	Chapter 25	Chapter 19
Lab 36: How much air can your lungs hold?	Chapter 34	Chapter 3	Chapter 13	Chapter 22	Chapter 20
Lab 37: How healthy are they?	Chapter 34	Chapter 3	Chapter 13	Chapter 22	Chapter 20
Lab 38: How do you digest protein?	Chapter 35	Chapter 2	Chapter 10	Chapter 20	Chapter 21
Lab 39: How does a body grow?	Chapter 36	Chapter 10	Chapter 15	Chapter 19	Chapter 22
Lab 40: Who needs a banana peel?	Chapter 37	Chapter 3	Chapter 4	Chapter 23	Chapter 23

Laboratory Manual

Using the Laboratory Manual

Student Edition

The activities in this laboratory manual are set up as *Classic* and *Design Your Own* labs. In a *Classic* activity, students are presented with a structured experiment having established parameters of results. In *Design Your Own* activities, students develop their own hypotheses based on provided background information and design activities and evaluation procedures for the hypotheses. In both kinds of activities, students use scientific methods to obtain data and answer questions. The basic format for the activities is described below.

Introduction: A brief introduction provides background information for each activity. Students might need to refer to the introduction for information that is important for completing an activity.

Objectives: Each statement listed in this section is a performance objective. You might want to use the objectives as a basis for evaluating student progress. Students can use them as a means for quickly determining what they will be doing in each activity.

Materials: Reagents, equipment, and supplies needed for each activity are listed here. Specific quantities of materials indicate minimum needs for each student or group. If you have very limited quantities of supplies and equipment, you might need to adjust the quantity of materials as listed or have students work in larger groups.

Procedure: (*Classic* activities) Instructions are often accompanied by diagrams for clarification. Emphasis is placed on developing student skill in carefully following directions and in observing, measuring, and recording data in an organized manner.

Hypothesis: (*Design Your Own* activities) Students write a hypothesis statement to express their expectations of the results and as an answer to the problem statement.

Plan the Experiment: (*Design Your Own* activities) Students plan how they will obtain their data, guided by the text in this section.

Cleanup and Disposal: Safe and appropriate handling and disposal of supplies is covered where appropriate.

Check The Plan: (*Design-Your-Own* activities) The steps in this section guide students in how to obtain their data. This section reminds students to have their procedure approved by the teacher before proceeding .

Data and Observations: This section includes tables and space for students to record their data and observations.

Analyze and Conclude: Students are asked to answer questions that require analysis of experimental data. Math skills and error analysis are included.

Write and Discuss: (*Design Your Own* activities) These questions provide material useful for classroom discussions or writing assignments based on the students' hypotheses and activities.

Inquiry Extensions: This section provides suggestions for additional activities that students may perform to further test a hypothesis, obtain more data for the current activity, or obtain data to answer problems related to the current activity.

In addition to the activities, the manual contains several other features, including a description of how to write a laboratory report, a section on the care of living things, diagrams of laboratory equipment, and information on safety in the laboratory.

Teacher Edition

The Teacher Edition supplies information designed to give you as much help as possible in preparing for activities. At the front of the Teacher Edition, you will find the following:

Teaching Strategy: This section gives ideas for modifying the activities to fit different time restrictions you might have. Methods for evaluating student performance are explained.

Alternatives to Dissection: This section describes alternatives if you do not want to teach dissection labs.

Working with Animals: This section gives instructions on the care of animals in the classroom and how to set up a marine aquarium for class use.

Safety and Disposal Guidelines: This listing of safety and disposal procedures and appropriate MSDS sheets will help you make the laboratory a safe place to work and learn. Included are basic procedures that should be followed while working in the laboratory. The information in this section should be stressed to students before any activities are undertaken.

Using the Laboratory Manual, continued

Preparation of Solutions: Solutions are listed by the number of the activity in which they are used. Preparation procedures, cautions, and amounts to make are indicated to aid you in the safe and economical use of reagents.

Course Materials List: All equipment, expendables, chemical supplies, and biological supplies needed to complete the activities are listed for a class of 30 students. Using this list, all materials needed for the entire year may be ordered, thus eliminating the problem of insufficient supplies.

Materials List per Lab: Using this list, you can easily tell how much of the materials each class will need to complete each activity. Again, materials are listed as equipment, expendables, chemical supplies, and biological supplies to aid you in planning for the use and securing of materials.

Suppliers: A list of suppliers has been included for your use in ordering materials.

How to Use the Student Models: Models and handouts needed to complete several activities are provided on pp. T24–T31.

Answers for Writing a Laboratory Report: At the back of the book, the Teacher Guide provides an answer key for each activity. The key contains answers to questions, sample data and labeled diagrams, helpful suggestions and teaching tips for preparing and teaching the activity, as well as a list of materials needed for the class. Suggestions for size of student groups appropriate for the activity and recommended time allotments are also provided. In addition, the Teacher Guide lists critical-thinking process skills students will use to develop the ability of thinking logically and abstractly.

Teaching Strategy

The activities in this laboratory manual might exceed the number of activities needed for a one-year course. You have the option to choose those best suited for your students and time schedule. The activities are designed to be as flexible as possible. Most can be completed in one laboratory period, although some might require observations over a period of time.

If time is limited, you might want to omit parts of an activity or reduce the number of trials or the time spent on each trial. The activities requiring model building can be conducted by students outside of class.

Using student teams might also allow for completion of activities that seem too lengthy for your school schedule. Each team could complete a different part of a three- or four-part activity and then share observed data.

Student progress can be evaluated through written answers in the *Analyze and Conclude* section or through the performance objectives in the *Objectives* section. For example, can a student properly record data from an activity so that it can be contributed to class totals? Can a student follow directions carefully so that activities proceed as planned and observations are valid?

Alternatives to Dissection

As a biology teacher, you probably want to foster the same thrill and excitement with nature in your students as you experience yourself. You want your students to appreciate and respect life and the diversity of organisms. You want them to develop an understanding of life processes and the interdependence of all living things. Above all, you want to see your students take responsibility for the quality of their own lives as well as the quality of life in our biosphere.

In order to achieve these goals, this laboratory manual presents some labs that provide students with the opportunity to observe life in its natural state. When students have the opportunity to work with live animals by examining their behavior, growth, development, social interactions, or ecology, they learn the complexity of biological systems. They learn about the life processes of various organisms. They learn important principles of behavior, physiology, and ecology. Students are encouraged to view living things, not as mere scientific subjects, expendable and unimportant, but as integral dynamic parts of the complex web of life.

Alternatives to dissection are important because students are taught that millions of species of life forms are being destroyed by habitat destruction and other human activities. Use of alternatives to dissection also satisfies concerns for animal welfare. Most importantly, current ethical issues, including AIDS, the greenhouse effect, in vitro fertilization, euthanasia, acid rain, abortion, and drugs have a biological basis. Because biological problems are problems of living systems, it is important that students have an opportunity to study live specimens.

Other alternatives to dissection, in addition to the activities provided in this laboratory manual, include videos, films, transparencies, models, charts, posters, and computer simulations of dissections. Students can be taken on field trips to observe animals at zoos, aquariums, and wildlife parks or refuges.

When you decide to teach labs that are alternatives to dissection, you are taking on the responsibility of having animals in your classroom. You will need to provide their food and housing. Make sure the animals are free of transmittable diseases and are obtained from a source where they have been maintained in good health. Review the custodial care of your animals, and supervise their care and handling by students. Plan who will be responsible for animal care on weekends, holidays, and vacations, and who will be economically responsible for the animals' needs, such as food and veterinary care. Students could be assigned library research projects concerning the care of any of the species you plan to introduce to the classroom.

Working with Animals

Care of Living Organisms

Teaching biology offers an opportunity to develop a respect for life by applying humane principles in the educational use of living organisms. Students need to understand the importance of providing good care for pets, animals used in class, and animals used in science projects. Students should not conduct activities that will cause pain, hardship, or death to animals. All activities involving living organisms should be conducted with care, discretion, and respect for those organisms. The National Association of Biology Teachers "Guidelines for the Use of Live Animals," published in *The American Biology Teacher*, Vol. 48, No. 2, Feb. 1986, are used as a standard throughout this laboratory manual. The guidelines are written in clear terms and can be used to stimulate a classroom discussion on the proper care and use of animals in society.

Some students might want to bring live animals to class, but you should discourage this practice unless there are adequate facilities and designated people to care for the animals. If adequate facilities are available, having animals in the classroom can be a positive learning experience for students. Students can learn the importance and responsibilities of providing food, space, fresh water, and adequate light and ventilation for animals. If students help with the care of classroom animals, keep a written log of who is feeding the animals, what food is being provided, and what quantities of food are being given.

Each kind of animal has its own environmental requirements. Pet stores and biological supply houses can provide you with specific care requirements when you purchase the animals. Allow animals to become adjusted to their surroundings before they are handled in laboratory activities.

Animal cages should be kept away from windows and drafts, heat registers, and air-conditioning ducts. Glass containers, such as terrariums and aquariums, should be kept out of direct sunlight so they do not overheat. Place predator species and prey species in separate areas of the classroom so they do not see or smell each other. Cages should be large enough to provide space for the animals to exercise, hide, and rest. Always keep animals in cages that lock securely, and keep the cages locked to ensure the safety of the animals. Students should not be allowed to handle the animals without supervision. Weekends and vacation periods can create problems if there has been no formal planning for the care of animals in the class. Some custodians might volunteer to care for the animals during a weekend or short vacation period. If a custodian cannot help, a regular group of volunteer caretakers will be needed. Encourage students to set up teams of volunteers for regular care of animals. During long vacation periods, responsible students should be available to take the animals home and care for them. Make sure students are aware of the nutritional requirements of any animals they take home.

Having live animals in the classroom is not a small responsibility. However, with careful planning, students can learn the responsibility and cooperation required when caring for living organisms.

Setting Up a Marine Aquarium

A saltwater aquarium to house specimens for a short period can be set up with a relative minimum amount of equipment and time. Glass aquariums holding 75 L are a good size for the classroom. Because salt water is a strong oxidizer, use an all-glass aquarium or one with a stainless steel frame.

Using natural ocean water is economical only if you live near the seashore. Otherwise, it is cheaper to buy salt mixtures to make synthetic seawater. Such mixtures may be purchased from biological supply houses, but can probably be obtained more inexpensively from a local pet store that sells tropical fish.

The water should have a pH between 8.0 and 8.3. If the pH is outside these bounds, it can be raised by adding calcium carbonate. A bubble aerator keeps the pH high by blowing off much of the carbon dioxide produced by the organisms.

A bed of gravel should be kept in the aquarium. You should buy a size of gravel that will not allow decaying particles of food or other material to be trapped. This will increase the oxygen demand and might lead to stress or death of aquarium occupants.

An efficient filter ensures that the water remains clear. Outside filters are preferable to filters placed in the water. Filtering the water through marble chips is a good way to keep the pH adjusted properly. Filters remove dissolved wastes by passing them over bacterial cultures within the filter's fibers. In addition to the filter, aeration should be added.

Heaters should be the glass-tube type. It is a good idea to seal all seams with silicone where the glass joins the plastic of the heater, so that the water cannot reach the inner metal parts. Heated aquariums (24 to 27°C) constantly evaporate water, making the salt content higher. A hygrometer can be used to keep the specific gravity at 1.025 by adding distilled water, as needed.

Additional information on keeping marine animals can be obtained from your local pet store. Local sources also usually have a wide variety of organisms from which to choose.

Safety and Disposal Guidelines

The activities in this manual are designed to minimize dangers in the laboratory, although there are no guarantees against accidents. However, careful planning and preparation, as well as being aware of hazards, can help keep accidents to a minimum.

General Safety: Review general safety rules listed in the Student Edition. These general rules should be emphasized to students before any laboratory work is done and should be reviewed periodically.

Additional Safety Guidelines

- At the beginning of the year, review the safety symbols used in the *Biology* textbook. Test students on their knowledge of these symbols.
- Review how to obtain all needed Material Safety Data Sheets. Print out all that will be needed for each lab.

In the Laboratory

1. Store chemicals properly.
   a. Separate chemicals by reaction type.
   b. Label all chemical containers: include purchase data, special precautions, and expiration date.
   c. Appropriately dispose of chemicals when outdated.
   d. Do not store chemicals above eye level.
   e. Wood shelving is preferable to metal. All shelving should be firmly attached to walls and have antiroll lips.
   f. Store only those chemicals that you plan to use.
   g. Hazardous substances require special storage containers.
2. Store equipment properly.
   a. Clean and dry all equipment before storing.
   b. Protect electronic equipment and microscopes from dust, humidity, and extreme temperatures.
   c. Label and organize all equipment.
3. Provide adequate work space for activities.
4. Provide adequate ventilation.
5. Post safety and evacuation guidelines and safety symbols.

6. Check to ensure that safety equipment is accessible and working properly.
7. Provide containers for disposing of chemicals, broken glass, other waste products, and biological specimens. Disposal methods must meet local guidelines.
8. Use hot plates for procedures requiring a heat source. If lab burners are used, a central shut-off valve for the gas supply should be accessible to you. Never use open flames when a flammable solvent is in the same room.

Before Each Activity

1. Perform activities yourself before assigning them to students to determine where students might have trouble. Previewing the activities in this manner also enables you to make note of symbols and safety cautions already incorporated into each activity.
2. Arrange the laboratory in such a way that equipment and supplies are easily accessible to students. Avoid confusion where solutions and reagents are being dispensed.
3. Have available only equipment and supplies necessary to complete the assigned activity. This practice helps eliminate the problem of students doing unauthorized experiments.
4. Review with students the procedure to be followed for each activity. Emphasize cautions found in the activities. Make students aware of specific safety symbols that are listed in the *Materials* section of each activity where potential safety problems may arise. Safety symbols that are used in all Glencoe science programs are shown on page *xiv* of the Student Edition. Post the appropriate MSDS sheet for the lab.
5. Review what students should do if an accident occurs. If chemicals need to be disposed of in a special place, remind students of proper disposal methods. Be sure all students know proper procedures to follow if an accident occurs and the proper way to use fire extinguishers, fire blankets, showers, and eyewash fountains. This equipment should be well marked and easily accessible.

During the Activity

1. Make sure that the laboratory is clean and free of clutter. Students' books, coats, and other personal items should be stored away from the laboratory tables.

2. Students should wear eye protection when heating substances or working with acids or bases that can cause burns. Many schools require that eye protection be worn at all times in the science laboratory. Know your school's policies and regulations and follow them.

3. Never allow students to work alone in the laboratory. If an accident would occur, there would be no one available to help the injured student.

4. Never allow students to use a scalpel or other cutting device with more than one sharp edge. When dissecting specimens, be sure students use dissecting pans to support their specimens. Hand-holding a specimen is "asking for" cuts.

5. If your microscopes require a separate light source, be sure students use proper lamps. Using reflected sunlight can damage the eye.

6. Use extreme caution if you use a pressure cooker for sterilization purposes. Turn off the heat source, remove the cooker, and allow the pressure to return to normal before opening the cover.

7. Students should never point the open end of a heated test tube toward anyone.

8. Remove broken or chipped glassware immediately. Use a whisk broom and dustpan to pick up broken glass. Large wads of wet cotton should be used to pick up small pieces of glass. Also immediately clean up any spills that occur. Dilute concentrated solutions with water before removing.

9. Be sure all glassware that is to be heated is a heat-treated type that will not shatter. If a gas flame is to be used as a heat source, the glassware should be protected from direct contact with the flame through the use of a wire gauze.

10. Remind students that heated glassware looks cool several seconds after heating but can still cause burns for several minutes.

11. Prohibit eating and drinking in the laboratory.

After the Activity

1. Be sure that the laboratory is clean. All work surfaces and equipment should be cleaned thoroughly after use.

2. Be sure students dispose of chemicals and broken glassware properly. Provide a container marked *Broken Glass*.

3. Be sure all hot plates and burners are turned off and disconnected before leaving the laboratory.

Disposal Guidelines

1. Bacterial and fungal cultures, used plastic petri dishes, cotton plugs, and contaminated growth medium should be autoclaved before disposal. Contaminated or used glassware should be autoclaved before being washed.

2. Obtain a current Material Safety Data Sheet (MSDS) for each chemical. Follow the chemical disposal recommendations. Be aware of local, state, and federal regulations for disposing of chemicals in municipal sewage systems or sanitary landfills.

3. Acids and bases can be neutralized by adding dilute sodium hydroxide to acids and dilute hydrochloric acid to bases until pH paper indicates that they are no longer strongly acidic or basic. Be aware that neutralization of strong acids and bases generates heat, so use caution by neutralizing slowly.

4. Follow MSDS recommendations for disposing of the organic chemicals used in this laboratory manual.

5. Solid wastes can be disposed of by placing them in a container suitable for disposal in a sanitary landfill. Be sure to follow applicable local regulations.

6. Broken glass should be placed in a separate, well-marked container.

Remember, a positive attitude toward safety on the part of students is imperative in operating a safe laboratory. Student attitude often reflects the teacher's attitude. Therefore, it is most important that you, as the teacher, always have a positive attitude toward safety and set good safety examples when conducting demonstrations and experiments.

Preparation of Solutions

Solutions used in the laboratory manual are listed in order by the number of the activity in which they are used. Preparation procedures, cautions, and amounts to make are also included. You might want to plan several weeks ahead so you will have all the solutions prepared.

Add solvents to the solutes. If a specific order of preparation is needed, it will be noted. Dissolve and mix thoroughly. Never add water directly to concentrated acid. Always add the acid to some water and then continue diluting. Because the diluting produces heat, it is advised that you add the acid by slowly pouring it along a stirring rod as you gently stir.

Unless directed otherwise, use distilled water in preparation of solutions requiring water. Using tap water might give erroneous results in the tests made by chemical solutions.
Mix solutions in a beaker or flask of greater capacity than the amount you are making. Usually 100- to 300-mL containers work well. It is better to make a little more than the exact amount needed because students might spill or waste some solution.

Sometimes it is more economical to buy chemicals in large quantities. Many chemicals can be stored for several years. However, certain chemicals become extremely hazardous, even explosive, with age. Know the age limitations of stored chemicals and the safe means of disposal of all chemicals in the laboratory. Flammable, volatile, and explosive chemicals should be stored in special secure areas and cabinets.

Solutions, once prepared, can be stored in large screw-cap or stoppered bottles. Glass is better than plastic because glass reacts with fewer chemicals. Storage containers should be cleaned with a low-sudsing detergent and rinsed well in distilled water before use.

If possible, ask your principal or department head to schedule some student laboratory assistants for your use. These students should be qualified to assist in lab preparations and instruction. They should be A/B students, mature, and responsible, and they should have taken a course in biology. The students should work directly under your supervision.

Lab	Solution	Preparation	Cautions
Lab 3	acid rain sample	Add 1 mL sulfuric acid to 99 mL distilled water.	Sulfuric acid is highly caustic. Use adequate ventilation when preparing solution.
Lab 4	nutrient agar	For ten plates: Add 5 g peptone, 3 g beef agar extract, and 15 g agar to 1 L warm water in a flask. Stir constantly, and slowly bring to a boil. When the liquid appears clear, pour agar into sterile petri dishes. When the agar has hardened, invert and refrigerate the petri dishes. Nutrient agar can also be stored in bottles. When needed, heat bottles in a pan of water until agar is melted. Sterile nutrient agar can be kept on a shelf for several years without contamination.	
Lab 6	tincture of iodine	Purchase from a pharmacy, or dissolve 70 g of iodine and 50 g of potassium iodide in 50 mL of distilled water. Then dilute to 1 L with 95% alcohol.	Iodine is toxic if ingested.
Lab 6	vitamin-C solution	Dissolve 1 g of ascorbic acid in approximately 500 mL of distilled water. Swirl to dissolve the solid. Dilute to make 1 L.	

Lab	Solution	Preparation	Cautions
Lab 6	starch solution	Place 4 g cornstarch in 10 mL distilled water. Stir to form a paste. Add to 1 L boiling water. Stir for 2 min, and allow to cool. Another option is to use starch-based (dissolvable) packing peanuts. Put 3 to 5 peanuts into 600 ml water.	
Lab 7	0.1M HCl	Carefully pour 1 mL concentrated hydrochloric acid into 99 mL distilled water.	Corrosive irritant. Flush with water if body contact occurs. Work under a hood, wearing gloves, goggles, and apron.
Lab 7	0.1M NaOH	To make 250 mL, add 1 g NaOH to 250 mL water.	Sodium hydroxide is very caustic. Avoid contact with eyes and skin. Flush with water if body contact occurs.
Lab 7	buffer 7	Purchase prepared buffer or make yourself. To make 0.1M diethanolamine, pH 10.3, combine 10.5 g (HOCH$_2$CH$_2$)2NH and 800 mL distilled water. Use NaOH or HCl to adjust pH to 10.3 and bring volume to 1 L with distilled water.	
Lab 7	liver solution	In an electric blender, mix 2 g fresh or frozen liver with 500–600 mL distilled water.	
Lab 7	egg solution	Blend one raw large or jumbo egg with 500–600 mL distilled water.	
Lab 7	gelatin solution	Prepare one packet unflavored gelatin according to package instructions, but do not refrigerate the gelatin to keep it liquid. If it is necessary to refrigerate the gelatin, add 25 percent more cold water to the mixture; this will prevent it from becoming completely firm.	
Lab 7	cucumber and/or fruit solution	Blend one cucumber or other fruit with 500–600 mL distilled water.	
Lab 8	agar with phenolphthalein	Prepare 1 L of non-nutrient agar according to the instructions on the bottle. Add 5 ml of phenolphthalein indicator. Just as the solution comes to a boil add NaOH (0.1M) until a distinct fuchsia color is achieved. The concentration of the HCl used in the lab must match the concentration of the NaOH used to prepare the agar. Pour into pans to a minimum depth of 3.5 cm, and allow to set.	
Lab 8	100 mL 0.1M solution of hydrochloric acid	*See Lab 7.*	*See Lab 7.*

Laboratory Manual

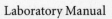

Lab	Solution	Preparation	Cautions
Lab 14	10% sodium dodecyl sulfate	Purchase prepared or buy the powder and mix a 10% solution (5 g SDS and 50 mL distilled water).	
Lab 19	caffeine solution	For caffeine powder: Add 2 g to 98 mL of distilled water for a 2% solution. If you want a .2% solution add 2 g to 198 mL of water. For stock caffeine solution (6.6%): Add 238 mL distilled water to 2 g instant coffee. 0.1%: Mix 130 mL distilled water with 2 mL stock solution. 0.3%: Mix 126 mL distilled water with 6 mL stock solution. 0.5%: Mix 122 mL distilled water with 10 mL stock solution.	
Lab 21	yeast mixture	Prepare one envelope of prepared yeast with 500 mL lukewarm water. Dilute by adding 10 mL of this preparation to 90 mL water.	
Lab 37	Biuret solution	Purchase prepared or make yourself. Dissolve 2.5 g of copper sulfate in 1 L water to prepare a $0.01M$ solution. Then prepare a second solution of $10M$ sodium hydroxide by dissolving 440 g of sodium hydroxide (CAUTION) in water then making up to 1 L. Before using, add 25 ml of the copper sulfate solution to 1 L of hydroxide solution.	Can irritate the eyes, skin, or respiratory tract, and should not be ingested. If contact occurs, flush the area with cold water. It can also stain clothing.
Lab 37	glucose solution	Place two to three spoonfuls of glucose in 500 mL distilled water. Exact amount is not important.	
Lab 37	protein solution	Dissolve 0.25 g gelatin in 100 mL boiling water. Add 50-100 mL cool water. Another option would be to add 1 g powdered egg albumin to a small amount of water. Stir slowly to avoid foaming. Bring the volume to 100 mL. For a more dilute solution, such as 0.1%, use 1 ml of 1% solution to 9 ml of water.	
Lab 37	simulated urine samples	Mix a solution of 50% glucose solution and 50% protein solution to create a sample that is positive for both protein and glucose. Add two drops yellow and one drop green food coloring.	
Lab 38	2% pepsin solution	Add 2 mL liquid (or 2 g powdered) pepsin to 98 mL distilled water.	
Lab 39	2% hydrochloric acid solution	Carefully pour 2 mL concentrated hydrochloric acid into 98 mL distilled water.	*See Lab 7.*

Course Materials List

Equipment

amino acid tables (60)
aquariums, large (2)
balances (10)
beakers, 50-mL (180); 250-mL (60); 500-mL (30); 1-L (30)
blenders (5)
calculators (30)
cellophane tape (15 rolls)
coins (penny, nickel, dime, quarter; 30 each) and bills ($1, $5; 30 each)
cover slips (120)
craft knives (30)
dissecting pans (30)
dissecting probes (30)
droppers (180)
electric fans (10)
flashlights (30)
flower identification books (field guides, 10)
forceps (15)
frying-pan covers (10)
funnels, small glass (60)
goggles (30)
graduated cylinders, 50-mL (30); 100-mL (30)
insect identification guides (field guides, 15)
jars, glass, small (15); large (60)
laboratory aprons (30)
lamps (20)
locking tongs (15)
magnifying lenses (30)
measuring tapes (15)
microscope slides, plain (60); with cell counters or grids (30)
microscopes, compound light (15)
music or voice recordings (15)
petri dishes with lids (100)
pH meters (15) or specific range pH papers (180)
pipettes, medium (30); large (180)
plastic chips, clear (25); red (25); yellow (25); blue (25)
plastic containers with lids, large (30)
portable CD or MP3 players with earphones (15)
preserved animal samples or photographs (15)
ring stands (10)
rubber balls (10)
rubber bulbs (10)
rubber mats (10)
rulers, metric (30); plastic (30)
scalpels (30)
scissors (30)
small blocks of wood (for brake and gas pedals) (20)
spoons, metal (30)
spray bottles (30)
stirring rods, glass (30)
stopwatches or watches with second hand (30)
straight pins (15)
strainers (30)
temperature probes (15)
test tube stoppers (120)
test tubes (120)
test-tube holders (30)
test-tube racks (30)
thermometers, non-mercury (30)
timers (15)
trowels (30)
tweezers (30)
weigh boats (60)
wire inoculating loops (30)

Expendables

aluminum foil (2 rolls)
animal envelopes (15 sets)
balloons, round, 12-inch (175)
blue litmus paper (250 strips)
boxes, medium to large (40)
candles (15)
card stock paper (30 sheets)
cardboard (30 pieces)
cheesecloth (10 m^2)
clay, modeling (1.5 kg each in two colors)
clear plastic bottles, 2-L (90)
clear plastic cups (30)
cloth squares of tightly woven cotton, polyester or silk (120)
colored gels or mylar (15)
corks (15)
cotton swabs (30)
diagram of gorilla, australopithecine, and human (30 copies)
diagram of pelvis and femurs of three animals (30 copies)
diagrams of the life cycles of ferns, mosses, and conifers (30 copies of each)
drawing of human and gorilla (30 copies)
envelopes of paper circles representing prey (15)
envelopes of UPC barcodes (30)
filter paper (70 sheets)
fine-point permanent markers (15)
gloves, latex or plastic
gloves, rubber (30 pairs)
glucose test strips (180)
glue, white (15 bottles)
granite gravel (7 kg)
graph paper (250 sheets)
hose, 1/2-inch plastic or vinyl (10 m)
index cards, white (500); blue (360); pink (360)
kitchen knives (30)
lens paper (15 sheets)
limestone chips (7 kg)
markers, colored (30 sets); permanent (30)
matches (15 books)
maze puzzles (180 copies)
metal coffee cans (clean; 15)
metal soup can (clean; 15)
newspaper apartment rentals or stock quotes (20 pages)
paper flags, 1 inch square; red on one side, white on the other (10)
paper plates (160)
paper towels (10 rolls)
paper, white (30 sheets); plain newsprint or butcher (20 sheets); grey (40 sheets)
pencils, colored (30 sets); lead with erasers (30); wax (30)
pens (30)
pH test strips (75)
plastic bags, sealable (180); open-top (60)
plastic containers with lids (250-mL yogurt containers, 90)
plastic knives (75)
plastic spoons (30)
plastic wrap, clear (5 rolls)
portraits, full facial, cut in half (30)
PVC pipe, 1/2 inch, 20 cm long (10)
rubber bands (30)
rubber cement (6 bottles)
shallow pans (30)
small rocks (1 kg)
tape, cellophane (15 rolls); duct (5 rolls); first aid (5 rolls); masking (15 rolls)
toothpicks (1 box)
tracing paper (30 sheets)
twist ties (60)
UPC barcodes from various products (40)
wire screen, 1/4-inch mesh, 10-cm squares (15)
wool socks (30 pairs)

Chemical Supplies

0.1M HCl (3.5 L)
0.1M NaOH (500 mL)
2% hydrochloric acid solution (3 L)
2% pepsin solution (3 L)
acid rain sample (500 mL)
agar, prepared with phenolphthalien (2 L); nutrient (enough for 60 plates)
aged tap water (10 L)
alcohols: isopropanol, pure ethyl alcohol, 151-proof liquor (75.5% alcohol) (60 mL of each)
alternative soil types, sand, clay, loam (1 bag each)
baking soda (sodium bicarbonate; 60 g)
bicarbonate of soda tablets (30)
Biuret solution (500 mL)
buffer 7 (750 mL)
caffeine solution (20 mL)
clear corn syrup (5 L)
cold water (14° to 18° degrees C)
detergents: 10% sodium dodecyl sulfate, dishwashing, shampoo, powdered soap (30 g each)
enzymes: meat tenderizer, pineapple juice, contact lens solution, fresh papaya, or crushed papaya tablets (10 g or mL of each)
food coloring (5 bottles)
glucose solution (1 L)
ice cubes
non-iodized salt (30 g)
petroleum jelly
potting soil, sterile (2 bags)
protein solution (1 L)
rubbing alcohol (160 mL)
sand (3.5 g)
simulated urine samples, 3 (1 L each)
soil (3.5 g)
starch solution (30 mL)
tincture of iodine (15 bottles)
vinegar (5 L)
warm water (26° to 30° C)
water, distilled (5 L)
water, tap, iced and hot

Biological Supplies

algae, living specimens (500 mL)
bananas, fresh (120); rotten (15)
boiled egg or firm tofu (75 g)
bread, with no preservatives (60 slices)
chicken eggs, extra-large or jumbo, hardboiled (30); unfertilized (30)
cucumber solution (750 mL)
DNA sources: onions, lima beans, strawberries, non-roasted wheat germ, calf thymus gland, dog testes, fresh liver, bacterial cultures, or yeast (30 g of each)
earthworms (60)
egg solution (750 mL)
Elodea samples (60 sprigs)
fern fronds (15)
flowers, large monocot (15); dicot (15)
food samples, such as rice cakes, peanuts, dried beans, dried cheese, marshmallows (15 of each)
fruit solution (750 mL)
gelatin solution (750 mL)
human skeleton (optional; 1)
juices and sports drinks with added vitamin C (500 mL of 4 types) with nutrition information for each (30 copies)
leaf litter (30 g)
live frogs (15)
live plants (30)
liver solution (750 mL)
methyl cellulose or 3% gelatin solution (20 mL)
moss samples (15)
mushrooms of different varieties purchased from local grocery store (enough to provide at least 15 whole caps, plus 50 g to dissect)
Nicotiana alata seeds (120)
orange juice (1 L)
pine cones, male and female (20 of each)
pond water (61 L)
prepared slide of onion root tip cells undergoing cell division (15)
seeds, flower (1 package); grass (30 g); lima bean (150)
simulated river water sample with copepods (5 L)
soil samples (30 L)
specimens: sea star, brittle star, sea urchin, sea cucumber, feather star, sea squirt and lancelets (15 sets)
sugar (10 g)
vitamin-C solution (1 L)
yeast mixture (50 mL)

Materials List per Lab

(quantities needed for a class of 30 students)

Lab	Equipment	Expendables	Chemical Supplies	Biological Supplies
Lab 1	droppers (30) laboratory aprons (30) goggles (30)	paper plates (60) plastic bags (sealable; 60) tape (15 rolls)	tap water	bread (with no preservatives; 60 slices)
Lab 2	electric fans (5) lamps (15) scissors (30) small beakers (15) or test tubes (15) thermometers (15) laboratory aprons (30) goggles (30)	clear plastic bottles (2-liter soda bottles; 60) small rocks (1 kg) clear plastic wrap (5 rolls) colored gels or mylar (15) index cards (60) masking tape (15 rolls) cellophane tape (15 rolls)	bicarbonate of soda tablets (30) sterile potting soil (2 bags) alternative soil types (sand, clay, loam; 1 bag each) water	flower seeds (1 package) grass seeds (30 g) lima bean seeds (150)
Lab 3	large glass jars (60) large dropper or pipette (30) light source (15) laboratory aprons (30) goggles (30)	granite gravel (7 kg) limestone chips (7 kg) pH test strips (75)	acid-rain sample (500 mL)	pond water (60 L) algae samples (500 mL)
Lab 4	rulers (30) calculators (30) petri dishes with lids (60) laboratory aprons (30) goggles (30)	graph paper (120 sheets) pencils (30) erasers (30) colored pencils (30 of 2 colors) masking tape (15 rolls) permanent markers (15)	nutrient agar (enough for 60 plates)	
Lab 5	rulers (30) calculators (30)	colored pencils (30 of 5 colors) pens (30) graph paper (30 sheets)		
Lab 6	50-mL beakers (180) droppers (180) laboratory aprons (30) goggles (30)	nutrition information for all beverages used (30 copies)	starch solution (30 mL) tincture of iodine (15 bottles)	vitamin C solution (1 L) orange juice (1 L) juices and sports drinks with added vitamin C (500 mL of 4 types)
Lab 7	pH meters (15) or specific range pH papers (150) stirring rods (30) 50-mL beakers (210) 500-mL beakers (30) 50-mL graduated cylinder (30) laboratory aprons (30) goggles (30)		0.1M HCl (500 mL) 0.1M NaOH (500 mL) water buffer 7 (750 mL)	liver solution (750 mL) egg solution (750 mL) gelatin solution (750 mL) fruit solution (750 mL) cucumber solution (750 mL)
Lab 8	250-mL beaker (30) timers (15) calculators (30) plastic ruler (30) laboratory aprons (30) goggles (30)	kitchen knives (30) plastic spoons (30) paper towels (1 roll)	agar *(See Preparation of Solutions, pp. T13–T15)* 0.1M solution of hydrochloric acid (3 L)	
Lab 9	test-tube holders (15) scales (6) temperature probes or thermometers (15) locking tongs (15) dissecting probes (15) straight pins or dissecting pins (15) graduated cylinders (15) weigh boats (12) laboratory aprons (30) goggles (30)	metal coffee cans (clean; 15) metal soup cans (clean; 15) corks (15) masking tape (15 rolls) matches (15 books) candles (15)		food samples, such as rice cakes, peanuts, dried beans, dried cheese, marshmallows (15 of each)

Lab	Equipment	Expendables	Chemical Supplies	Biological Supplies
Lab 10	large glass jars (60) scales (6) rulers (30) scissors (30) small glass funnels (60) test tubes (60) lamps (20) laboratory aprons (30) goggles (30)	medium to large box lined with white paper (20) medium to large box lined with grey paper (20)	aged tap water (10 L) baking soda (sodium bicarbonate; 60 g)	*Elodea* samples (enough for 60 jars)
Lab 11	microscopes (15) calculators (15) laboratory aprons (30) goggles (30)	colored pencils		prepared slides of onion root tip cells undergoing cell division (15)
Lab 12	petri dishes (40) metric ruler (30) laboratory aprons (30) goggles (30)	filter paper (40 sheets) fine-point permanent markers (15)	water	*Nicotiana alata* seeds (120)
Lab 13	scissors (30)	index cards (360 of two colors—blue and pink) pencils (30)		
Lab 14	balances (6) blenders (5) beakers, 50-mL (30) and 250 mL (15) stirring rods (15) small strainer large test tubes (30) funnel wire inoculating loops (15) laboratory aprons (30) goggles (30)	paper plates (100) cheesecloth filter paper (30 sheets)	iced water (4 L) ice cubes (2 L) hot water (4 L) non-iodized salt (30 g) various types of alcohol including isopropanol, pure ethyl alcohol, 151-proof liquor (75.5% alcohol) (60 mL of each) various detergents including 10% sodium dodecyl sulfate (*See Preparation of Solutions, pp. T13–T15*), different brands of dish detergent or shampoo without conditioner or other additives, or powdered soaps (30 mL of each) various sources of enzymes including meat tenderizer, pineapple juice, contact lens solution, fresh papaya, or crushed papaya tablets (10 g or mL of each)	various sources of DNA including onions, lima beans, strawberries, non-roasted wheat germ, calf thymus gland, dog testes, fresh liver, bacterial cultures, or yeast (30 g of each)
Lab 15	magnifying lenses (15) rulers (30) laboratory aprons (30) goggles (30)	UPC barcodes (40)		
Lab 16	amino acid table (60 photocopies)			

Lab	Equipment	Expendables	Chemical Supplies	Biological Supplies
Lab 17	clear plastic chips (25) red chips (25) yellow chips (25) blue chips (25) calculators (15) stopwatches or watches with second hand (15)	colored pencils graph paper pages of newspaper apartment rentals or stock quotes (20; 15 for lab exercise, 5 for prep) sheet of plain paper, the same size as the newspaper (20; 15 for lab exercise, 5 for prep) envelopes of paper circles representing prey (15) forceps or pencils with eraser (15)		
Lab 18	calculators (30) scissors (30) rulers (30)	diagrams of gorilla, australopithecine and human scale drawing of human and gorilla (30; *See How To Use the Student Models, pp. T24–T31*) card stock paper with large diagrams of a gorilla and a human (30; *See How To Use the Student Models, pp. T24–T31*) diagram of pelvis and femurs of three animals (30; *See How To Use the Student Models, pp. T24–T31*) glue		human skeleton (optional)
Lab 19	coin sets (penny, nickel, dime, quarter) and bills ($1 and $5) (15 sets of each) reference material	pen (30) pencils (30) index cards (165) animal envelopes (15 sets; *See How To Use the Student Models, pp. T24–T31*		
Lab 20	funnels (30) clean droppers (60) large beakers (30) small beakers (30) graduated cylinders (15) microscopes (15) slides with cell counter or slides with grids (30) cover slips (30) metric rulers (15) laboratory aprons (30) goggles (30)	cloth squares of tightly woven cotton, polyester or silk (120)		simulated river water sample with cocpepods (5 L)
Lab 21	microscopes (15) slides and cover slips (60) droppers (30) table lamps (15) laboratory aprons (30) goggles (30)	latex or plastic gloves (30 pairs)	warm water (26° to 30° C) cold water (14° to 18° C) 1 g per L caffeine solution (20 mL)	sample of pond water (1 L) yeast mixture (50 mL) methyl cellulose or 3% gelatin solution (20 mL) sugar (10 g)

Lab	Equipment	Expendables	Chemical Supplies	Biological Supplies
Lab 22	magnifying lenses (30) dissecting probes (30) large plastic containers with lids (30) rulers or stiff sticks (15) laboratory aprons (30) goggles (30)	paper towels white paper (30 sheets) round balloons (15) cotton balls (1 package) modeling clay tape (15 rolls)		mushrooms of different varieties purchased from local grocery store (enough to provide at least 15 whole caps, plus 50 g to dissect)
Lab 23	scalpels (15) forceps (15) droppers (15) petri dishes (15) magnifying lenses (15) laboratory aprons (30) goggles (30)	paper towels colored pencils (15 sets) diagrams of the life cycles of ferns, mosses, and conifers (30; *See How To Use the Student Models,* pp. T24-T31)	water	fern fronds (15) moss sample (15) pine cones, (male and female; 15 of each)
Lab 24	electric fans (10) pipettes (30) scissors (30) small beakers (30) laboratory aprons (30) goggles (30)	small plastic bags (not the zippered kind; 60) twist ties (60)	food coloring (5 bottles) petroleum jelly water	live plants (30)
Lab 25	flower identification books (field guides; 10) droppers (15) magnifying lenses (15) microscopes (15) slides (15) cover slips (15) scalpels (30) metric rulers (30) laboratory aprons (30) goggles (30)	paper towels (1 roll) cellophane tape (15 rolls) lens paper (15 sheets) colored pencils (15 sets)	water	large flowers (15 monocot, 15 dicot)
Lab 26	rulers (15) preserved samples or photographs of an animal (15) supplementary resource materials on each animal sample (15) laboratory aprons (30) goggles (30)	pencils (30) plain, unlined paper (15 sheets) selection of full facial portraits cut in half lengthwise (30) tracing paper (30 sheets) glue or rubber cement cellophane tape (15 rolls) clay in two colors (1 kg of each color) plastic knives (15)		
Lab 27	stopwatches (30) clean spray bottles or eye droppers (30) flashlights (30) non-mercury thermometers (30) rulers (30) laboratory aprons (30) goggles (30)	paper towels (5 rolls) shallow pans (30) cardboard (30 pieces)	water soil (3.5 kg) sand (3.5 kg)	earthworms (60)

Lab	Equipment	Expendables	Chemical Supplies	Biological Supplies
Lab 28	scissors (30) trowels (30) lamps (15) magnifying lenses (15) jars (15 large, 15 small) forceps (30) spoons (30) insect identification guides (15) laboratory aprons (30) goggles (30)	2-liter clear plastic bottles (30) cheesecloth or plastic wrap (2 rolls) rubber bands (30) 1/4-inch mesh wire screen (15 10-cm squares)		soil samples (30 L) leaf litter (30 g) pine cones (30)
Lab 29	rulers (30) laboratory aprons (30) goggles (30)	glue paper (30 sheets) markers/colored pencils		specimens: sea star, brittle star, sea urchin, sea cucumber, feather star, sea squirt and lancelets (15 sets)
Lab 30	table tops large aquariums (2) laboratory aprons (30) goggles (30)	paper towels (2 rolls) pencils with erasers (30)	water	live frogs (15)
Lab 31	petri dishes (30) tweezers (30) magnifying lenses (30) metric rulers (30) microscopes (15) microscope slides (30) cover slips (30) balances (10) laboratory aprons (30) goggles (30)	paper towels (2 rolls) small plastic knives (30) clear plastic cups (30) rubber gloves (30 pairs) aluminum foil (2 rolls)	distilled water (5 L) clear corn syrup (5 L) vinegar (5 L)	unfertilized chicken eggs (the larger the better; 30) hardboiled chicken egg (the larger the better; 30)
Lab 32	1-L beakers (30) non-mercury thermometers (90) stopwatches (30) scissors (30) craft knives (30) laboratory aprons (30) goggles (30)	wool socks (30 pairs) plastic containers with lids (yogurt containers, 250 mL; 90) rubber bands (90) graph paper (30 sheets) colored pencils (30 each of 3 colors)	hot water (from tap) room temperature water	
Lab 33	portable CD or MP3 players with earphones (15) music or voice recordings (15) stopwatches (15)	pencils or markers (15) copies of maze puzzle (180; *See How To Use the Student Models, pp. T24–T31*)		
Lab 34	rubber bulbs (10) ring stands (10) stopwatches (10) laboratory aprons (30) goggles (30)	1/2-inch plastic or vinyl hose (10 M) 1/2-inch PVC pipe (10 pieces cut to 20 cm each) paper flags, red on one side, white on the other (10) cellophane tape (10 rolls) duct tape (5 rolls) first aid tape (5 rolls)		
Lab 35	stopwatches (10) frying-pan covers (for steering wheel; 10) small blocks of wood (20) rubber mats (10) rubber balls (10) laboratory aprons (30) goggles (30)			

Materials List per Lab, continued

Lab	Equipment	Expendables	Chemical Supplies	Biological Supplies
Lab 36	metric rulers (15) non-mercury thermometers (15) measuring tapes (15) laboratory aprons (30) goggles (30)	balloons, round (12-inch maximum diameter; 150) string (15 m)		
Lab 37	test tubes (180) test-tube racks (30) plastic droppers (30) large pipettes for each sample (180) laboratory aprons (30) goggles (30)	glucose test strips (180) wax pencils (30) white paper or paper towels (60 sheets)	Biuret solution (500 mL) glucose solution (1 L) protein solution (1 L) simulated urine samples (1 L of each) *(See Preparation of Solutions, pp. T13–T15.)*	water
Lab 38	test-tube racks (30) rulers (30) graduated cylinders (30) test tubes with stoppers (120) stirring rod (glass; 30) laboratory aprons (30) goggles (30)	blue litmus paper (250 strips) plastic knives (30) wax pencils (30)	2% pepsin solution (3 L) 2% hydrochloric acid solution (3 L)	boiled eggs or firm tofu (75 g)
Lab 39	metric rulers (30) calculators (30)	colored pencils (30 each of 3 colors) graph paper (30 sheets)		
Lab 40	laboratory aprons (30) goggles (30)	sealable plastic bags (120) permanent markers (30) paper towel (3 rolls) toothpicks (1 box) cotton swabs (30)	water rubbing alcohol (150 mL)	fresh bananas (120) rotten bananas (15)

Suppliers

American Science & Surplus
P.O. Box 1030
Skokie, IL 60076
(847) 647-0011
www.sciplus.com

Arbor Scientific
P.O. Box 2750
Ann Arbor, MI 48106-2750
(734) 477-9370
www.arborsci.com

Bio-Rad Laboratories
2000 Alfred Nobel Dr.
Life Science Group
Hercules, CA 94547
(800) 876-3425
www.biorad.com

Carolina Biological Supply Co.
2700 York Road
Burlington, NC 27215
(800) 334-5551
www.carolina.com

Chem Scientific, LLC
1250 Washington St.
Norwood, MA 02062
(888) 527-5827
www.chemscientific.com

Edmund Scientifics
60 Pearce Ave.
Tonawanda, NY 14150-6711
(800) 728-6999
www.scientificsonline.com

Fisher Science Education
4500 Turnberry
Hanover Park, IL 60133
(800) 955-1177
www.fisheredu.com

Flinn Scientific
P.O. Box 219
770 N. Raddant Rd.
Batavia, IL 60510
(800) 772-8700
www.flinnsci.com

Frey Scientific
P.O. Box 8105
100 Paragon Parkway
Mansfield, OH 44903
(800) 225-FREY
www.freyscientific.com

Nasco Science
901 Janesville Avenue
P.O. Box 901
Fort Atkinson, WI 53538-0901
(800) 558-9595
www.enasco.com

Nebraska Scientific
3823 Leavenworth St.
Omaha, NE 68105-1180
(800) 228-7117
www.nebraskascientific.com

PASCO Scientific
10101 Foothills Blvd.
Roseville, CA 95747-7100
(800) 772-8700
www.pasco.com

Sargent-Welch/VWR
Scientific Products
P.O. Box 5229
Buffalo Grove, IL 60089-5229
(800) SAR-GENT
www.sargentwelch.com

Science Kit and Boreal Laboratories
777 East Park Dr.
P.O. Box 5003
Tonawanda, NY 14150
(800) 828-7777
www.sciencekit.com

VWR CanLab
2360 Argentina Rd.
Mississauga, Ontario L5N5Z7
(800) 932-5000
www.vwrcanlab.com

Ward's Natural Science Establishment, Inc.
5100 W. Henrietta Road
P.O. Box 92912
Rochester, NY 14692-9012
(800) 962-2660
www.wardsci.com

How To Use the Student Models

Paper models for Labs 18, 19, 23, and 33 can be found on this page and on pages T25–T31. Photocopy the models for your students to use during these activities.

Lab 18

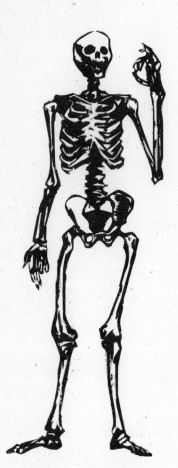

Human Skeleton

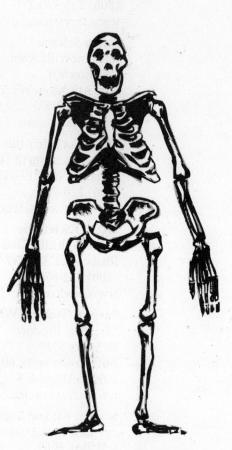

Austrolopithecine Skeleton

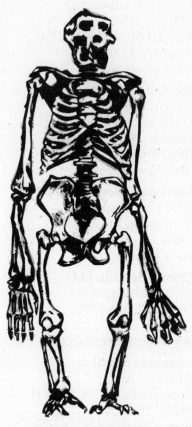

Modern Gorilla Skeleton

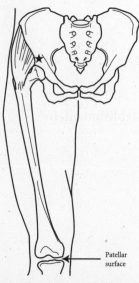

Human Hip and Femur

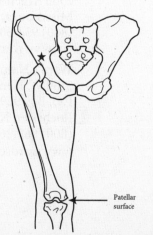

Austrolopithecine Hip and Femur

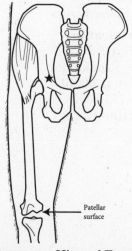

Chimpanzee Hip and Femur

Laboratory Manual

Lab 18

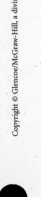

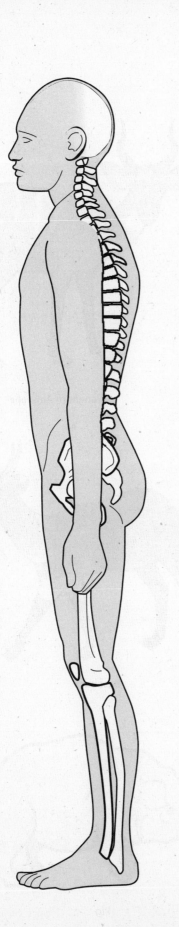

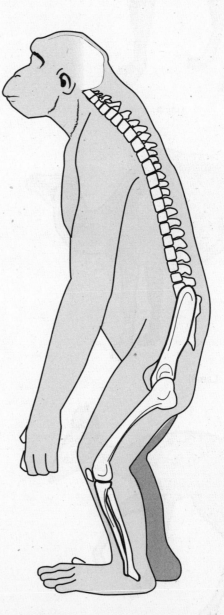

Lab 19

Llama

Pronghorn Antelope

Camel

Bushbuck

Dik-dik

Pig

Lab 19

African Buffalo

Hippopotamus

Sheep

Giraffe

Mountain Goat

Lab 23

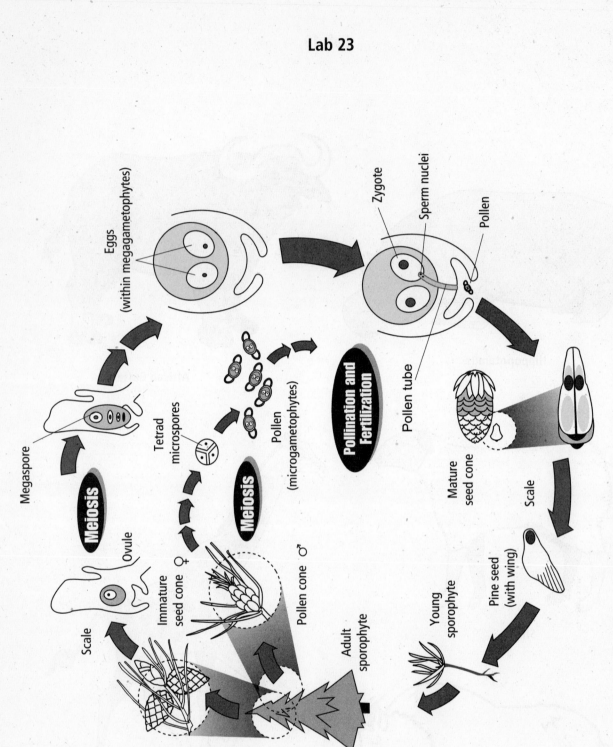

Conifer Reproductive Cycle

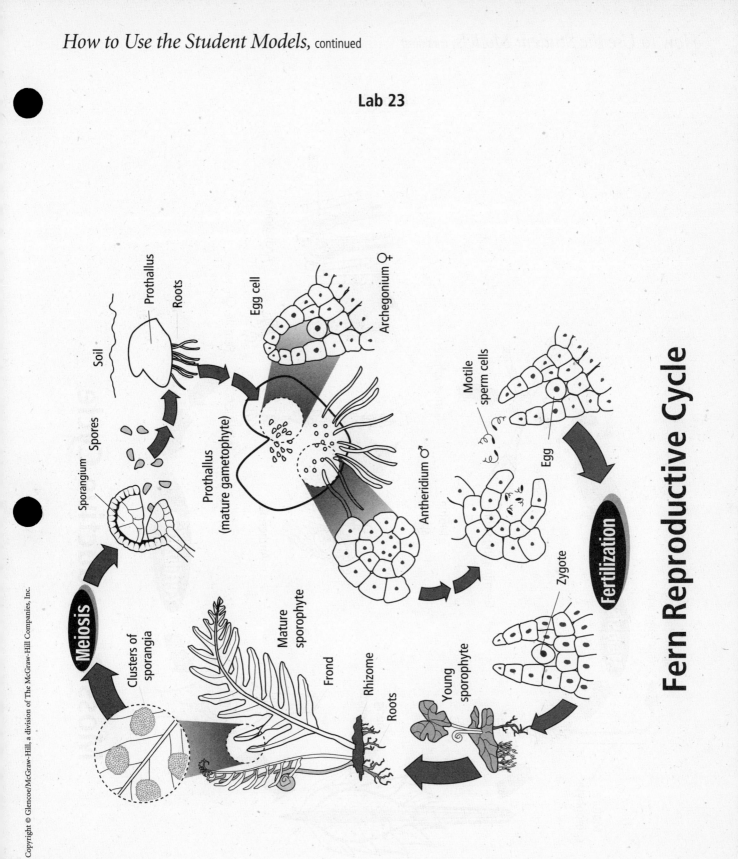

Fern Reproductive Cycle

Lab 23

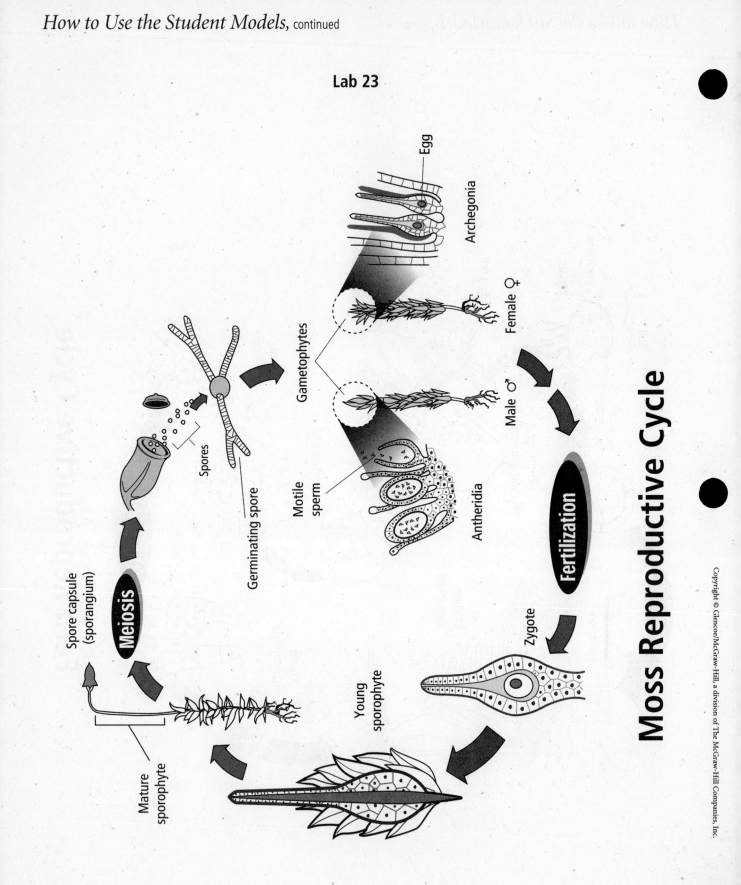

Moss Reproductive Cycle

Egg

Archegonia

Female ♀

Male ♂

Gametophytes

Motile sperm

Antheridia

Germinating spore

Spores

Meiosis

Spore capsule (sporangium)

Mature sporophyte

Young sporophyte

Zygote

Fertilization

Lab 33

Answers for Writing a Laboratory Report

for Student Pages vii–viii

1. The purpose of the experiment was to test the effect of overcrowding on the growth of plants.
2. Materials needed for the experiment include 16 bean seeds, three containers, potting soil, water, metricruler, and graph paper.
3. **Step 1** Fill three containers with equal amounts of potting soil. Label the three containers *Container 1, Container 2,* and *Container 3,* respectively.

   Step 2 Plant one bean seed in Container 1, five bean seeds in Container 2, and ten bean seeds in Container 3. Plant all seeds at the same depth.

   Step 3 Water all three containers with equal amounts of water. Place all three containers in a well-lit room.

   Step 4 For the next two weeks, water each container once a day. Use an equal amount of water in each container.

   Step 5 Measure the heights of the plants in each container every day for the next two weeks. Calculate the average height of the plants in each container each day. Record these measurements in a table.

   Step 6 After two weeks, plot the data in your table on a graph.
4. The least amount of growth was observed in Container 3. Living space in Container 3 had to be shared among ten growing plants. As a result, no plant had enough space to grow well.
5.

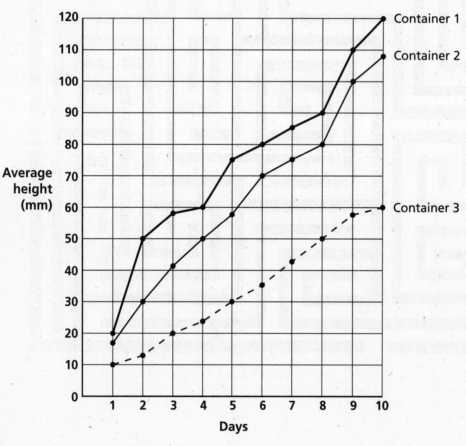

Laboratory Manual

Glencoe Science

LAB MANUAL

Biology

Biology Online
glencoe.com

Mc Graw Hill **Glencoe**

New York, New York   Columbus, Ohio   Chicago, Illinois   Peoria, Illinois   Woodland Hills, California

The McGraw-Hill Companies

Send all inquiries to:
Glencoe/McGraw-Hill
8787 Orion Place
Columbus, OH 43240-4027

ISBN-13: 978-0-07-874720-5
ISBN-10: 0-07-874720-1

Printed in the United States of America.

1 2 3 4 5 6 7 8 9 10 11 045 11 10 09 08 07 06

Table of Contents

Laboratory Manual

How to Use This Laboratory Manual

Working in the laboratory throughout the course of the year can be an enjoyable part of your biology experience. This laboratory manual is a tool for making your laboratory work both worthwhile and fun. The laboratory activities are designed to fulfill the following purposes:

- to stimulate your interest in science in general and especially in biology
- to reinforce important concepts studied in your textbook
- to allow you to verify some of the scientific information learned during your biology course
- to allow you to discover for yourself biological concepts and ideas not necessarily covered in class or in the textbook readings
- to acquaint you with a variety of modern tools and techniques used by today's biological scientists

Most importantly, the laboratory activities will give you firsthand experience in how a scientist works.

The activities in this laboratory manual are of two-types: Classic or Design Your Own. In a *Classic* activity, you will be presented with a problem and will use the steps of the experiments to draw conclusions. In *Design Your Own* activities, you will be given background information, and then will be asked to develop your own hypothesis and design activities and evaluation procedures to test it. In both kinds of activities, you will need to use scientific methods to obtain data and answer questions.

The basic format for the activities is described below. Understanding the purpose of each section will help guide you as you work through each activity.

Introduction: A brief introduction provides background information for each activity. You might need to refer to the introduction for information that is important for completing an activity.

Objectives: The list of objectives is a guide to what will be done in the activity and what will be expected of you.

Materials: The materials section lists the supplies you will need to complete the activity. Check with your teacher to obtain these materials.

Procedure: (*Classic* activities) The procedure gives you step-by-step instructions for carrying out the activity. Many steps have safety precautions. Be sure to read these statements and obey them for your own and your classmates' protection. Unless told to do otherwise, you are expected to complete all parts of each assigned activity. Important information needed for the procedure, but that is not an actual procedural step, is also found in this section.

Hypothesis: (*Design Your Own* activities) You will write a hypothesis statement to express your expectations of the results and as a response to the problem statement.

Plan the Experiment: (*Design Your Own* activities) In this section, you will plan how to obtain data, guided by the background information provided to you.

Check the Plan: (*Design Your Own* activities) Have your procedure approved by the teacher before proceeding.

Record the Plan: (*Design Your Own* activities) Write your experimental plan, and sketch your equipment setup.

Data and Observations: This section includes tables and space to record data and observations.

Analyze and Conclude: In this section, you will draw conclusions about the results of the activity just completed. Rereading the introduction before answering the questions might be helpful.

Write and Discuss: (*Design Your Own* activities) This section provides material you might use in a classroom discussion or homework assignment based on the activity.

Inquiry Extensions: This section includes ideas for ways to extend the activity or plan related experiments.

In addition to the activities, this laboratory manual has several other features—a description of how to write a lab report, a section on the care of living things, diagrams of laboratory equipment, and information on safety that includes first aid and a safety contract. Read the section on safety now. Safety in the laboratory is your responsibility. Working in the laboratory can be a safe and fun learning experience and can help you to understand and enjoy biology.

Writing a Laboratory Report

When scientists perform experiments, they make observations, collect and analyze data, and formulate generalizations about the data. When you work in the laboratory, you should record all your data in a laboratory report. An analysis of data is easier if all data are recorded in an organized, logical manner. Tables and graphs are often used for this purpose. A written laboratory report should include all of the following elements.

TITLE: The title should clearly describe the topic of the report.

HYPOTHESIS: Write a statement to express your expectations of the results and as an answer to the problem statement.

MATERIALS: List all laboratory equipment and other materials needed to perform the experiment.

PROCEDURE: Describe each step of the procedure so that someone else could perform the experiment following your directions.

RESULTS: Include in your report all data, tables, graphs, and sketches used to arrive at your conclusions.

CONCLUSIONS: Record your conclusions in a paragraph at the end of your report. Your conclusions should be an analysis of your collected data.

Read the following description of an experiment, then answer the questions.

All plants need water, minerals, carbon dioxide, sunlight, and living space. If these needs are not met, plants cannot grow properly. A biologist thought that plants would not grow well if too many were planted in a limited area. To test this idea, the biologist set up an experiment. Three containers were filled with equal amounts of potting soil. One bean seed was planted in Container 1, five seeds in Container 2, and ten seeds in Container 3. All three containers were placed in a well-lit room. Each container received the same amount of water every day for two weeks. The biologist measured the heights of the growing plants every day. Then the average height of the plants in each container each day was calculated and recorded in a table. The biologist then plotted the data on a graph.

1. What was the purpose of this experiment?

_____

2. What materials were needed for this experiment?

_____

3. Write a step-by-step procedure for this experiment.

_____

_____

_____

_____

_____

_____

_____

_____

_____

4. Table 1 shows the data collected in this experiment. Based on these data, state a conclusion for this experiment.

_____

_____

_____

_____

Table 1

Average Height of Growing Plants (mm)										
	Day									
Container	1	2	3	4	5	6	7	8	9	10
1	20	50	58	60	75	80	85	90	110	120
2	16	30	41	50	58	70	75	80	100	108
3	10	12	20	24	30	35	42	50	58	60

5. Plot the data in **Table 1** on a graph. Show average height on the vertical axis and the days on the horizontal axis. Use a different colored pencil to graph the results of each container.

Care of Living Things

Caring for living things in a biology laboratory can be interesting and fun, and it can help develop the respect for all life that comes only from firsthand experience. In a room with an aquarium, terrarium, healthy animals, or growing plants, there is always some observable interaction between organisms and their environment. There are many species of plants and animals that are suitable for a classroom, but having them should be considered only if proper care will be taken so that the organisms not only survive, but thrive. Before growing plants or bringing animals into a classroom, find out if there are any health or safety regulations restricting their use, or if there are any applicable state or local laws governing live plants and animals. Also, do not consider cultivating any endangered or poisonous species. A biological supply house or local pet store will provide growing tips for plants or literature on animal care when these organisms are purchased.

Evaluating Resources

Before bringing any live specimens into a new environment, check with your teacher to see if their basic needs will be met in their new location. Plants need either sunlight or grow lights. Animals must be placed in well-ventilated areas out of direct sunlight and away from the draft of open windows, radiators, and air conditioners. For both animals and plants, a source of fresh water is essential. Consider the likely fluctuation in temperature over weekends and holidays, and who will care for the plants or animals during those times.

Setting Up an Aquarium

A closed system such as an aquarium supports a variety of animals and plants and can be maintained easily if set up correctly. A 10- or 20-gallon tank can be a suitable home for about 5 to 10 tropical fish or even more of the temperate goldfish. An air pump, filter, heater, thermometer, and aquarium light (optional) need to be in working order.

First fill an aquarium with a layer of gravel, then fill with water. If using tap water, let the water stand a day before putting any fish in the tank. During cooler months, adjust the thermostat of the heater to bring the water to the desired temperature before adding fish. Most fish require temperatures of 20° to 25°C. An inexpensive pH kit purchased from a pet store will test the acidity of the water and guide the maintenance of a healthy pH.

Choose fish that are compatible with one another. A pet-store clerk can help in the selection. It is worth purchasing a scavenger fish, such as a catfish, or an algae eater that will help keep the tank clean of algae. Snails are also helpful for this purpose. After purchasing, keep fish in the plastic bag containing water in which they came. Float the bag in the aquarium until the water reaches the same temperature, then slowly let the fish swim out of the bag. Some fish, such as guppies, eat their young. A smaller brood tank can be placed inside the aquarium to keep the mother separated from the young.

One person should be responsible for feeding the fish. Feed fish sparingly. Overfeeding is not healthy for the fish; also, it clouds the tank and causes unnecessary decay. Weekend or vacation food should also be available. These are slow-dissolving tablets that can feed the fish over vacations.

Plants can be added to an aquarium as well. *Elodea, Anacharia, Sagittaria, Cabomba,* or *Vallianeria* grown in a fish tank also are useful for many biology lab activities. Monitor their growth carefully and trim plants if growth is excessive. Some fish and snails might nibble on the plants, causing them to break apart and decay. Decay introduces bacterial populations that can endanger the fish, so be sure to remove any decaying plant matter.

Variations on an aquarium include setting up a "balanced aquarium" with fish, plants, and scavengers in balance so that no pump or filter is necessary. This usually takes more planning and maintenance than a filtered tank. More maintenance is needed also for a marine aquarium because of the corrosive nature of salt water. However, if specimens of marine organisms are readily available, creating such a mini-habitat is well worth the effort.

Keeping Mammals in a Classroom

Keeping mammals takes more consideration and commitment of time and expense. A small mammal such as a gerbil, guinea pig, hamster, or rabbit can be kept in a classroom, at least for a short time. Explore the possibility of dwarf breeds that are more at home in a small space. However, many mammals are sensitive, social mammals that form bonds and attachments to people. Life in a small cage alone most of the time is not suitable for a long and healthy life. For short periods of time, however, small animals can be kept in a cage, provided it is clean and large enough. Find out the exact nutritional needs of the animals; feed them on a regular schedule and provide fresh water daily. Some animals require dry food supplemented with fresh foods, such as greens. However, these foods spoil more rapidly, and uneaten portions must be removed. Provide a cage large enough for the animal, as well as materials for bedding, nesting, and gnawing. Clean the cages frequently. Letting urine and feces collect in a cage fosters the growth of harmful bacteria. Animals in a cage also require an exercise wheel. Lack of space combined with overeating can make an animal overweight and lethargic. Handle animals gently. Under no circumstances should animals be exposed to harmful radiation, drugs, toxic chemicals, or surgical procedures.

Many times students want to bring a pet or even a wild animal that they have found into the classroom for observation. Do so only with discretion and if a proper cage is available. Protective gloves and glasses should be worn while handling any animals with the potential to bite. Be sure to check with local park rangers or wildlife specialists for any wildlife restrictions that may apply. Return any wild animals to their environment as soon as possible after observations.

Growing Plants in the Classroom

To successfully grow plants in a classroom, have on hand commercial potting soil, suitable containers such as clay or plastic pots, plant fertilizer, a watering can, and a spray bottle for misting. Always put a plant in the correct size container. One that is too large will encourage root growth at the expense of the stem and leaves. Place bits of broken clay or gravel in the bottom of the pot for drainage, then add potting soil and the plant. Place in a warm, well-lighted area and supply water. Give careful attention to a new plant to assess its adaptation to its new environment. Pale leaves might indicate insufficient light, yellowing

leaves indicate overwatering, and dropping leaves usually indicate insufficient humidity. Fertilize only as directed.

With little special attention, plants such as geraniums, begonias, and coleus can be easily and inexpensively grown in a classroom. These plants are hardy and can withstand fluctuations in light and temperature. From one hardy plant, many cuttings can be made to demonstrate vegetative propagation. A cutting of only a few leaves on a stem will develop roots in 2 to 4 weeks if it is placed in water or given root-growth hormone powder.

These plants not only add color to a classroom but are useful in biology experiments as well. The dense green leaves of geraniums are especially useful for extracting chlorophyll or showing the effects of light deprivation. The white portions of variegated coleus leaves are good for showing the absence of photosynthesis with a negative starch-iodine reaction. Pinch back the flower buds as they begin to form to encourage fuller leaf growth.

Larger plants such as a fig (*Ficus*), dumbcane (*Dieffenbachia*), cornplant (*Dracaena*), Norfolk Island pine (*Araucaria*), umbrella plant (*Schefflera*), or various philodendrons adapt well to low-light conditions and so do not need frequent watering. However, make sure humidity is suitable to avoid dropping leaves. More exotic plants might be best suited to a small-dish garden but will need special care because there is less soil to hold moisture.

During winter months, a dish garden of forced bulbs, such as paperwhite narcissus, can be easily grown by placing the bulbs in a container of water left in a cool, dark place. Blooms will appear in 3 to 4 weeks. In the early spring, shoots of early flowering shrubs, such as forsythia and pussy willow, may be forced. Cut off some healthy shoots when buds appear, wrap in wet newspaper, then bring indoors and immerse cut ends in a tall vase or jar. Also buds of fruit trees, such as apple, plum, or peach, will produce leaves and flowers in this way. Be sure to maintain shoots by changing water when necessary.

Laboratory Equipment

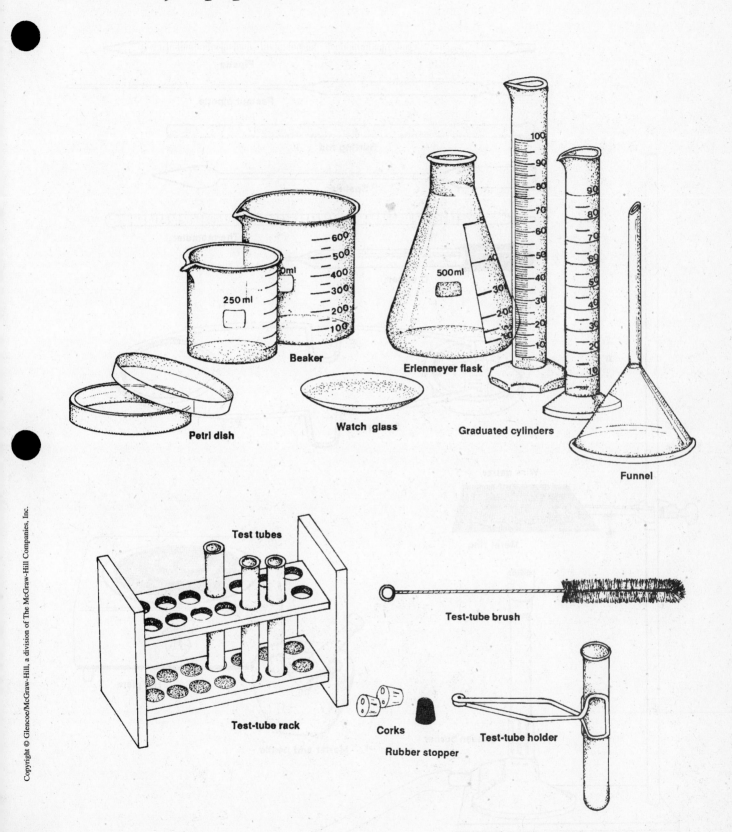

Beaker

250 ml

Erlenmeyer flask

500ml

Petri dish

Watch glass

Graduated cylinders

Funnel

Test tubes

Test-tube brush

Test-tube rack

Corks

Rubber stopper

Test-tube holder

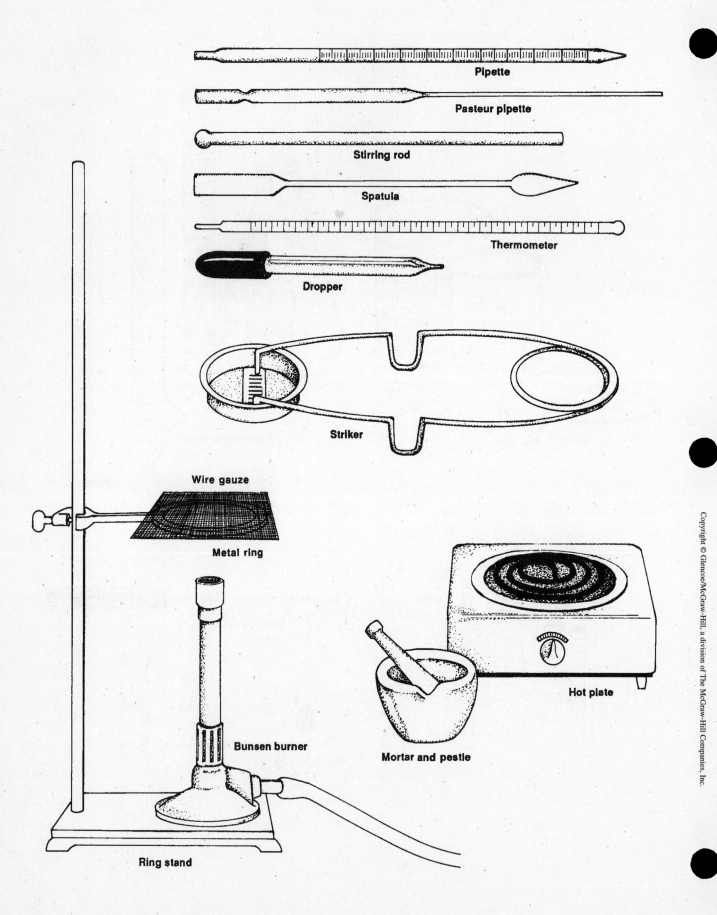

Pipette

Pasteur pipette

Stirring rod

Spatula

Thermometer

Dropper

Striker

Wire gauze

Metal ring

Bunsen burner

Mortar and pestle

Hot plate

Ring stand

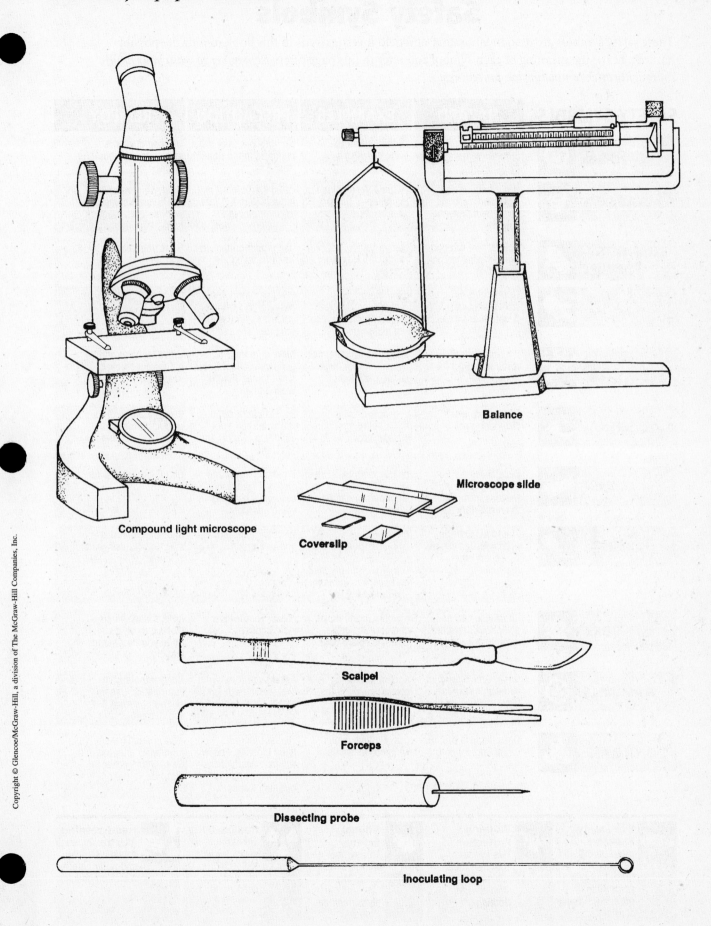

Balance

Compound light microscope

Microscope slide

Coverslip

Scalpel

Forceps

Dissecting probe

Inoculating loop

Safety Symbols

These safety symbols are used in laboratory and field investigations in this book to indicate possible hazards. Learn the meaning of each symbol and refer to this page often. *Remember to wash your hands thoroughly after completing lab procedures.*

SAFETY SYMBOLS	HAZARD	EXAMPLES	PRECAUTION	REMEDY
DISPOSAL	Special disposal procedures need to be followed.	certain chemicals, living organisms	Do not dispose of these materials in the sink or trash can.	Dispose of wastes as directed by your teacher.
BIOLOGICAL	Organisms or other biological materials that might be harmful to humans	bacteria, fungi, blood, unpreserved tissues, plant materials	Avoid skin contact with these materials. Wear mask or gloves.	Notify your teacher if you suspect contact with material. Wash hands thoroughly.
EXTREME TEMPERATURE	Objects that can burn skin by being too cold or too hot	boiling liquids, hot plates, dry ice, liquid nitrogen	Use proper protection when handling.	Go to your teacher for first aid.
SHARP OBJECT	Use of tools or glassware that can easily puncture or slice skin	razor blades, pins, scalpels, pointed tools, dissecting probes, broken glass	Practice common-sense behavior and follow guidelines for use of the tool.	Go to your teacher for first aid.
FUME	Possible danger to respiratory tract from fumes	ammonia, acetone, nail polish remover, heated sulfur, moth balls	Make sure there is good ventilation. Never smell fumes directly. Wear a mask.	Leave foul area and notify your teacher immediately.
ELECTRICAL	Possible danger from electrical shock or burn	improper grounding, liquid spills, short circuits, exposed wires	Double-check setup with teacher. Check condition of wires and apparatus.	Do not attempt to fix electrical problems. Notify your teacher immediately.
IRRITANT	Substances that can irritate the skin or mucous membranes of the respiratory tract	pollen, moth balls, steel wool, fiberglass, potassium permanganate	Wear dust mask and gloves. Practice extra care when handling these materials.	Go to your teacher for first aid.
CHEMICAL	Chemicals that can react with and destroy tissue and other materials	bleaches such as hydrogen peroxide; acids such as sulfuric acid, hydrochloric acid; bases such as ammonia, sodium hydroxide	Wear goggles, gloves, and an apron.	Immediately flush the affected area with water and notify your teacher.
TOXIC	Substance may be poisonous if touched, inhaled, or swallowed.	mercury, many metal compounds, iodine, poinsettia plant parts	Follow your teacher's instructions.	Always wash hands thoroughly after use. Go to your teacher for first aid.
FLAMMABLE	Open flame may ignite flammable chemicals, loose clothing, or hair.	alcohol, kerosene, potassium permanganate, hair, clothing	Avoid open flames and heat when using flammable chemicals.	Notify your teacher immediately. Use fire safety equipment if applicable.
OPEN FLAME	Open flame in use, may cause fire.	hair, clothing, paper, synthetic materials	Tie back hair and loose clothing. Follow teacher's instructions on lighting and extinguishing flames.	Always wash hands thoroughly after use. Go to your teacher for first aid.

Eye Safety
Proper eye protection should be worn at all times by anyone performing or observing science activities.

 **Clothing Protection**
This symbol appears when substances could stain or burn clothing.

 Animal Safety
This symbol appears when safety of animals and students must be ensured.

Radioactivity
This symbol appears when radioactive materials are used.

Handwashing
After the lab, wash hands with soap and water before removing goggles

Student Lab/Activity Safety Form

Student Name: _____

Date: _____

Lab/Activity Title: _____

In order to show your teacher that you understand the safety concerns of this lab/activity, the following questions must be answered after the teacher explains the information to you. You must have your teacher initial this form before you can proceed with the activity/lab.

1. How would you describe what you will be doing during this lab/activity?

2. What are the safety concerns associated with this lab/activity (as explained by your teacher)?

- _____
- _____
- _____
- _____
- _____

3. What additional safety concerns or questions do you have?

Adapted from Gerlovich, et al. (2004). The Total Science Safety System CD, JaKel, Inc.
Used with Permission.

Design Your Own
Lab 1

What makes mold grow?

Have you ever opened a bag of bread and found green or white mold growing on the bread? Where did this mold come from? What types of conditions are better for mold growth, and what measures can you take to avoid them? In this laboratory exercise, you will design an experiment to test one of the conditions that might result in bread growing mold.

Problem
Determine what conditions are ripe for the growth of mold on bread.

Objectives
- Write a hypothesis.
- Develop an experiment to test the hypothesis.
- Control variables during the experiment.
- Draw conclusions about the formation of mold on bread.

Safety Precautions

WARNING: *Do not eat any food in a science lab. Do not open the sealed bags. The release of mold spores can aggravate allergies, asthma, and other medical conditions.*

Possible Materials
paper plates
dropper
bread (with no preservatives)
plastic bags (sealable)
tap water
tape

Hypothesis
Use what you know about the mold found on bread to write a hypothesis indicating what factors influence the formation of mold.

_____

_____

_____

_____

Copyright © Glencoe/McGraw-Hill, a division of The McGraw-Hill Companies, Inc.

Plan the Experiment

1. Read and complete the lab safety form.
2. Make a list of the factors that might influence the formation of mold on bread. Be sure to test the factors you listed in your hypothesis.
3. Decide on a procedure for testing your hypothesis. In the space provided, write your procedure for testing the factors. Include a list of the materials you will use.
4. Identify the independent variable, dependent variable, constants, and control group.
5. Decide how you will record your data and when you will record it. Design a data table to collect information about the presence of mold over a period of six days. Be sure to collect quantitative data that can answer these types of questions: How many colonies are there? What is the size of each colony?

Check the Plan

1. Be sure that a control group is included in your experiment and that the experimental groups vary in only one way.
2. Make sure your teacher has approved your experimental plan before you proceed.
3. When you have completed your experiment, dispose of materials as directed by your teacher.

Record the Plan

In the space below, write your experimental procedure and make a sketch of your experimental setup.

Design Your Own **Lab** 1, **What makes mold grow?** continued

Data and Observations

1. Use the space below to create a data table of your findings, including information about the presence of mold.

Analyze and Conclude

1. How did the appearance of the two slices of bread change over the six days?

_____

_____

_____

2. How can you explain differences in the appearance of the bread?

_____

_____

_____

3. What was the manipulated variable in your experiment? Why was it necessary to control all the other variables other than this one?

_____

_____

_____

4. Describe the control in your experiment. What did the control show?

_____

_____

_____

_____

5. Error Analysis What were some possible sources of error in your experiment?

_____

_____

_____

6. Exchange your procedure and data with another group in your class for peer review. Discuss any differences in the results.

_____

_____

_____

Write and Discuss

Write a short paragraph describing your findings and indicating whether or not they support your hypothesis. Discuss any questions your findings might have raised.

_____

_____

_____

Inquiry Extensions

1. Many health-food stores and supermarkets now sell organic baked goods with no preservatives, but many brands of bread continue to use them. How well do these preservatives work at reducing the time it takes for mold to form? Design an experiment that tests the differences between the formation of mold on bread with preservatives and organic bread.

2. What other conditions could influence the rate of mold formation? Temperature? Exposure to sunlight v. artificial light? Contact with other foods? Design an experiment to test one of these hypotheses, or a hypothesis that you develop on your own, and report your results to the class.

Design Your Own
Lab 2

How does your biome grow?

The environmental factors that affect the growth of an organism can be grouped into two categories—biotic and abiotic. Biotic factors are living organisms in the environment. Abiotic factors include naturally occurring substances in the soil, such as chemicals and nutrients, as well as water, sunlight, and temperature. In this lab, you will create a model biome and study the effects of abiotic factors on germinating plants.

Problem
What impact do abiotic factors have on biomes?

Objectives
- Form a hypothesis about the impact of abiotic factors on a biome.
- Design an experiment to test your hypothesis.
- Identify a control to the experiment.
- Make a model of a biome.
- Create a data table.
- Draw conclusions.

Safety Precautions

Wash your hands thoroughly with soap and water after handling the soil.

Possible Materials
bicarbonate of soda tablets
clear plastic bottles (2-L soda bottles)
clear plastic wrap
colored gels or mylar
electric fan
flower seeds
grass seeds
lima bean seeds
index cards
lamps
masking tape
sterile potting soil
alternative soil types (sand, clay, loam)
scissors
small rocks
small beaker or test tubes
tape
water

Hypothesis
Use what you know about ecosystems and ecology to write a hypothesis indicating the effect of an abiotic factor of your choice on the germination of plants in a model biome.

_____

_____

_____

_____

Plan the Experiment

1. Read and complete the lab safety form.
2. Choose which biome you wish to simulate. Be sure that your biome is indicated in your hypothesis.
3. Decide on a procedure to use to test the impact of an abiotic factor on your simulated biome.
4. Identify the independent variable, dependent variable, constants, and control group.
5. Describe how you will measure and record your data.

Check the Plan

1. Make sure your teacher has approved your experimental plan before you proceed.
2. Be sure that a control group is included in your experiment and that the experimental group varies in only one way.
3. Observe and record the impact of abiotic factors on the biotic components of your simulated biome. Be sure to make sketches each day of your biome and the changes you observe. Be detailed in your drawings. Provide quantitative observations (using measurements).
4. When you have completed the experiment, ask your teacher whether you should continue to make long-term observations or dispose of the organisms as he or she directs.

Record the Plan

In the space below, write your experimental procedure and make a sketch of your experimental design.

Design Your Own **Lab** 2, **How does your biome grow?** continued

Data and Observations

1. Use the space below to create a data table of your findings.

Analyze and Conclude

1. On which abiotic factor did you focus? Why?

_____

_____

_____

2. Did this abiotic factor seem to have a significant impact on the dependent variable in your simulated ecosystem? Explain.

_____

_____

_____

3. Describe the control in your experiment. What was held constant in the control? Why was it set up that way?

_____

_____

_____

_____

4. How does your experiment relate to biomes and abiotic factors in nature?

_____

_____

5. **Error Analysis** What are some possible sources of error in your experiment?

_____

_____

6. Exchange your procedure and data with another group in your class. What do their data show about the biome they chose to simulate? What conclusions can you draw about the abiotic factors in a biome?

_____

_____

7. What are the limitations of the design of this experiment? Are there additional factors at work?

_____

_____

Write and Discuss
Write a short paragraph describing your findings and indicating whether or not they support your hypothesis. Discuss any questions your results have raised.

_____

_____

_____

_____

_____

Inquiry Extensions
1. Describe the rainfall pattern and abiotic factors that make up the biome you live in. How do these factors impact the plants, animals, and agriculture in your area?
2. If you were to maintain your biomes in the classroom or at home, what abiotic factors would you change from your original model? Make a prediction about what you would observe under the new conditions.

Design Your Own
Lab 3

Do freshwater biomes respond differently to acid rain?

Your state happens to be downwind from a volcano that recently ejected large amounts of ash and sulfur and, as a result, rainwater in your area has been unusually acidic. You are conducting research for your state's water resources department to see how different types of lakes are affected by this acidic rainwater.

Problem

Design an experiment that will test how acid rain impacts algae in a freshwater ecosystem. You might want to explore a variety of ecosystems found in different areas of the country or your state, such as a pond or lake with limestone bedrock or a pond or lake with granite bedrock.

Objectives

- Design an experiment to assess the impact of acid rain on a freshwater pond.
- Conduct the experiment and record data.
- Interpret data and draw conclusions.

Safety Precautions

WARNING: *Use caution with the acid rain samples—they might cause chemical burns. Be sure to keep lamps away from water sources to avoid a potential shock hazard.*

Possible Materials

pond water
algae samples
limestone chips
acid rain sample
large glass jars (2)
granite gravel
pH test strips
large dropper or pipette
light source

Hypothesis

Use what you know about pH and acid rain to write a hypothesis indicating what impact acid rain will have on an aquatic environment.

_____

_____

_____

_____

Plan the Experiment

1. Read and complete the lab safety form.

2. Choose the type of gravel you will use to line your pond: granite or limestone.

3. Decide on a procedure to use when setting up your pond environment and for testing the pH of the water.

4. Identify the independent variable, dependent variable, constants, and control group.

5. Decide how you will record your data and when you will record it. Design a data table to collect information about the pH of the water, the time that has elapsed, and the status of the algae growing and living in your pond.

6. Determine the length of time needed to observe your samples.

Check the Plan

1. Be sure that a control group is included in your experiment and that the experimental group varies in only one way.

2. Make sure the teacher has approved your experimental plan before you proceed.

3. Observe the impact that acid rain has on the growth of algae in your simulated pond environment.

4. When you have completed the experiment, dispose of the pond water as instructed by your teacher. Be sure to wash your hands with soap and water after you are done.

Record the Plan

In the space below, write your experimental procedure and make a sketch of your experimental setup.

Design Your Own **Lab 3, Do freshwater biomes respond differently to acid rain?** continued

Data and Observations

1. Use the space below to create a data table of your findings, including the length of time that has passed, the pH of the water each day, and the status of the algae that is growing in the pond water.

Analyze and Conclude

1. How did the pH of your simulated pond change from day to day?

_____

_____

_____

_____

2. What impact did the stone lining at the bottom of your pond have on the pH of the water?

_____

_____

_____

_____

3. How did the algae in your pond survive? Describe any changes in the appearance of the algae. Explain possible reasons for what you found.

_____

_____

_____

4. What was the control in your experiment? What did the control show?

_____

_____

_____

_____

5. Error Analysis What were some possible sources of error in your experiment?

_____

_____

_____

_____

6. For the peer review process, exchange your procedure and data with a group that used the same stone as you did and with a group that used the other option. Does comparing your data with the data from the other groups indicate that the presence of granite as opposed to limestone can affect the pH in a pond environment? What conclusion can you draw?

_____

_____

_____

_____

Write and Discuss

Write a short paragraph describing your findings and indicating whether or not they support your hypothesis. Discuss any questions your results might have raised.

_____

_____

_____

_____

Inquiry Extensions

1. How does temperature impact the pH of a sample? Design an experiment that examines the impact of temperature on the pH of pond water.

2. Why should you be concerned about the impact of acid rain on ponds, lakes, and streams? How does the pH of pond water ultimately impact your life as a teenager in the United States?

Classic
Lab 4

How can you show a population trend?

Populations exhibit growth because of births as well as immigration. The rate at which populations grow depends on many factors. One factor is the rate at which the species can produce offspring. Factors that limit populations, called limiting factors, include predators, disease, food supply, and availability of suitable habitat.

Some of these factors depend on the density of the population, while others do not. Density-dependent factors include the availability of food, the occurrence of disease, stress, light availability, and predators. Density-independent factors include extreme weather, fires, seasonal changes, floods, and changes to habitat (such as tree cutting).

Objectives

- Culture bacterial colonies to track population growth.
- Graph population data, choosing appropriate scales and titles.
- Compare and contrast populations and the factors that affect growth.

Materials

pieces of graph paper (4)
ruler
pencil
eraser
calculator
colored pencils
petri dishes with lids (2)
nutrient agar
masking tape
permanent marker

Safety Precautions

WARNING: *Use protective gloves if the petri dishes were recently removed from the autoclave—they might be hot. Always wash your hands after handling the cultured petri dishes.*

Procedure
Part A. Counting a Bacterial Population

1. Read and complete the lab safety form.
2. Prepare two growth chambers. Sterilize two petri dishes and their tops.
3. Place the agar into both petri dishes. Cover one of the dishes, and seal it with tape. This will be your control. Using the marker, label a piece of masking tape with the letter *A*, and affix it to the bottom of the dish.
4. Run your fingertips along the surface of the agar in the second petri dish.
5. Place the top on the dish, and seal the edges with tape. Label a piece of masking tape with the letter *B*, and affix it to the bottom of the dish.
6. Use **Table 1** to record the information you will be gathering.
7. After two days, examine both petri dishes. Be aware of the development of small, white, yellow, or cream-colored dots. Each dot represents a bacterial colony. *Do not open or compromise the seal on your petri dishes.*
8. Count the number of bacterial colonies on the surface of the agar that you touched. Compare this number with the number of colonies on the surface you did not touch. If separate colonies cannot be counted, look at the percentage of the surface covered in bacteria.
9. Dispose of your petri dishes as instructed by your teacher. Do not open them. Clean the table surface with a disinfectant.

Part B. Exponential Growth of Bacteria

1. **Table 2** shows the growth of a bacterial population from a single bacteria cell.
2. Choose appropriate axes, and plot the data on a sheet of graph paper.
3. Make a best fit line to connect the dots.
4. Give your graph a title, and label the axes.

Part C. Limiting Factors

1. **Table 3** contains data gathered on the number of breeding male fur seals from 1902 to 1950.
2. Choose appropriate axes, and plot the data on a sheet of graph paper.
3. Make a best fit line to connect the dots.
4. Give your graph a title, and label the axes.

Part D. Predator-Prey Relationships

1. **Table 4** contains data on the population of snowshoe hares and lynxes during the course of 100 y.
2. Choose appropriate axes, and plot the data on a sheet of graph paper.
3. Plot the data for the hare in one color and the data for the lynx in another color.
4. Give your graph a title, and label the axes.

Part E. Human Population Growth

1. **Table 5** contains figures on the population of humans on Earth since A.D. 1.
2. Choose appropriate axes, and plot the data on a sheet of graph paper.
3. Make a best fit line to connect the dots.
4. Give your graph a title, and label the axes.

Data and Observations

Table 1

Bacterial Growth	
Petri Dish	Number of Colonies/ Percentage of Surface Covered
(A) Control	
(B) Contaminated	

Table 2

Growth of Bacteria	
Time	Number of Cells
0 min	1
20 min	2
40 min	4
60 min	8
80 min	16
100 min	32
120 min	64
240 min	4,096

Table 3

Fur Seal Population	
Year	Population
1902	1000
1911	1200
1915	3000
1917	4500
1923	3000
1924	3100
1925	3000
1932	8400
1933	8400
1936	10,700
1937	9100
1940	10,800
1942	11,000
1945	10,400
1946	11,000
1950	9500

Classic **Lab** 4, **How can you show a population trend?** continued

Table 4

Hare and Lynx Populations		
Year	Population	
	Snowshoe Hare	Lynx
1850	38	20
1854	90	15
1856	75	30
1857	88	32
1862	40	22
1865	30	28
1870	25	25
1872	160	40
1875	120	80
1880	40	41
1883	20	35
1885	78	33
1888	90	48
1890	87	52
1892	40	38

Table 5

Human Population	
Year	Estimated or Projected Population
A.D. 1	300,000
1200	450,000
1650	500 million
1800	1 billion
1930	2 billion
1959	3 billion
1974	4 billion
1986	5 billion
1999	6 billion
2013	7 billion
2027	8 billion

Analyze and Conclude

1. What did the bacteria consume as food in this experiment?

_____

_____

2. Bacteria require very little to grow and multiply. Why are there not large, visible colonies of bacteria like those in the petri dish on the things we use every day?

_____

_____

3. What type of curve fits the data for the growth of the bacteria in **Table 2**? How does the curve change with the rate of bacteria growth?

_____

_____

4. **Error Analysis** What were possible sources of error in your experiment?

_____

_____

5. What type of curve best fits the data for the fur seal population? Describe what happened to the population.

_____

_____

6. What happened to the fur seal population? Use the terms *limiting factor* and *carrying capacity* in your answer.

_____

_____

7. Describe the relationship you see in the graph of the snowshoe hare and the lynx population.

_____

_____

8. What type of relationship do hares and lynxes have? How would you explain their respective growth cycles?

_____

_____

9. Describe the growth of the human population in the past 350 y. Why might scientists and others be concerned about this pattern?

_____

_____

_____

Inquiry Extensions

1. Research more information on the growth of the human population. How have advances in medicine and technology contributed to the trend on the graph? Research information on death rates and birth rates of the human race. Write a short paragraph describing how technology and medicine have affected the population growth of humans.

2. What other predator-prey relationships can you think of that might exist in the wild? Research their population data, and graph their population trends. Compare the trends.

Classic Lab 5

How do we measure biodiversity?

The number of different species in an area is an indication of the area's biodiversity. It is important to preserve biodiversity because it contributes to the balance of an ecosystem. The more diverse an ecosystem, the more stable it is. In addition, diverse ecosystems are a source of recreation and beauty.

In this lab, you will look at biomass and rainfall data from four different sites in the same ecosystem. The rainfall was consistent among the sites. The biomass at each site was measured for a period of 11 years. The biomass was determined by collecting, drying, and measuring the mass of all the plant material that could be clipped from a 0.3-m² area. Your job will be to analyze the data and develop a hypothesis to explain the changes in biodiversity in the communities at these sites.

Objectives
- Analyze data from four test sites.
- Infer trends in biodiversity.
- Predict which environmental factors impact biodiversity.

Materials
pen
graph paper
ruler
colored pencils
calculator

Procedure
1. Read and complete the lab safety form.
2. The data below is from four vegetation areas.
   Community 1 is native grassland.
   Community 2 was a farm 20 years ago.
   Community 3 was a farm field 31 years ago.
   Community 4 was a farm 54 years ago.
   The data is the average grams of biomass measured in each area.
3. Plot this data on a graph. Show biomass per year on the vertical axis on the left side and rainfall on the vertical axis on the right side. Use separate colors for the lines for each community and a fifth color for rainfall. Choose an appropriate scale, and label each axis.

Table 1

Annual Average Grams of Biomass				
Year	Community 1 (grams biomass per 0.3 m²)	Community 2 (grams biomass per 0.3 m²)	Community 3 (grams biomass per 0.3 m²)	Community 4 (grams biomass per 0.3 m²)	Total Annual Precipitation (cm)
1982	138	126	130	136	76.78
1983	142	123	132	145	99.24
1984	140	127	123	131	93.85
1985	138	125	135	133	80.42
1986	144	124	132	136	93.01
1987	77	5	37	56	41.30
1988	76	4	24	54	48.46
1989	112	15	38	78	58.58
1990	134	33	83	103	83.95
1991	140	56	83	105	92.43
1992	142	80	113	122	75.39

Source: David Tilman and John A. Downing, Department of Ecology, Evolution and Behavior, University of Minnesota, 1994

Data and Observations

1. Attach your graph to the space below.

Analyze and Conclude

1. What type of organisms would you expect to make up the biomass in each community?

   _____

   _____

2. Which community do you think is most diverse? Why?

   _____

   _____

   _____

Classic **Lab** 5, **How do we measure biodiversity?** continued

3. What correlation do you see between the precipitation data and the biomass in each community? What does this indicate?

_____

_____

_____

_____

4. Which community had the greatest change in biomass? Which had the least? What are the reasons for this?

_____

_____

_____

_____

_____

5. Which community recovered most rapidly after the drought? Which had the slowest recovery?

_____

_____

_____

_____

6. **Error Analysis** What were possible sources of error in this exercise?

_____

_____

7. Look back at your answer to question 2. How does the diversity in a community impact its biological stability?

_____

_____

_____

Inquiry Extensions

1. What other types of drastic abiotic changes could affect a community? Choose one and describe how each community in this study could be impacted and how it might rebound.

2. In terms of biodiversity, what impact could humans have on the communities described in the lab? Design a study that would trace the impact humans could have on one community. What elements would you focus on in your study? Your study can take place over a series of years.

Design Your Own

Lab 6

How much vitamin C are you getting?

Vitamin C, like other vitamins found in food, is an organic compound that serves as a helper molecule for a variety of chemical reactions in your body. Also known as ascorbic acid, vitamin C helps keep your skin and gums healthy.

Vitamin C will react with iodine and remove its amber color. If vitamin C and starch are both present, iodine will react first with the vitamin C. When the vitamin C is gone, the iodine will react with the starch, producing a blue color. This means that when the concentration of vitamin C is higher, more iodine is needed to create a color change.

Problem

Many fruit juices contain vitamin C naturally. Recently, manufacturers have started to add vitamin C to some juices and sports drinks. Select five juices, and test each one to determine which has the highest concentration of vitamin C.

Objectives

- Make predictions about the amounts of vitamin C in a variety of drinks.
- Design an experiment to compare the amounts of vitamin C in these beverages.
- Measure how different substances react in the presence of iodine.
- Draw conclusions about the nutritional value of the beverages.

Safety Precautions

WARNING: *Iodine is toxic if ingested. It will also stain hands and clothing.*

Possible Materials

50-mL beakers (6)
plastic droppers
starch solution
tincture of iodine
vitamin-C solution
orange juice
juices and sports drinks with added vitamin C (4)
additional information provided by your teacher

Hypothesis

Use what you know about vitamin C and fruit juices, and what you have been told through advertising, to write a hypothesis indicating which drink you think has the most vitamin C and why.

_____

_____

_____

_____

Plan the Experiment

1. Read and complete the lab safety form.
2. Choose five drinks to test for vitamin C. Be sure to test the drink listed in your hypothesis.
3. Decide on a procedure for testing the drinks for the amount of vitamin C. Write your procedure below. Include the materials you will use.
4. Identify the independent variable, dependent variable, constants, and control.
5. Decide how you will record your data. Design a data table to collect the information. You might want to include a column for your predicted rankings of vitamin-C content for each item.

Check the Plan

1. Make sure your teacher has approved your experimental plan before you proceed.
2. Be sure that a control is included in your experiment.
3. When you have completed the experiment, dispose of the liquids as directed by your teacher.

Record the Plan

In the space below, write your experimental procedure and make a sketch of your experimental setup.

Design Your Own **Lab 6, How much vitamin C are you getting?** continued

Data and Observations

1. Use the space below to create a data table of your findings, including the type of drink, the number of drops of iodine, the predicted ranking, and the actual ranking.

Analyze and Conclude

1. Which sample had the highest level of vitamin C? Which had the lowest?

_____

_____

2. Based on your observations, do drinks with natural vitamin C vary greatly from drinks with added vitamin C?

_____

_____

3. What does the vitamin-C content of the beverages imply about their nutritional value?

_____

_____

_____

4. Describe the control in your experiment. What did the control show?

_____

_____

_____

5. Error Analysis What were some possible sources of error in your experiment?

_____

_____

_____

_____

6. Compare your data to the nutritional information label provided for each drink. Do your results match the nutritional information provided? Does the information match your prediction? Compare serving sizes and the percentage of the Recommended Dietary Allowance (RDA) of vitamin C listed on the label. How much of each drink would have to be consumed in order to obtain the RDA of vitamin C?

_____

_____

_____

_____

Write and Discuss

Write a short paragraph describing your findings and indicating whether or not they support your hypothesis. Did any of the juices stand out as being higher in vitamin C than the others? Discuss any questions your results might have raised.

_____

_____

_____

_____

Inquiry Extensions

1. Packaged or processed foods are usually marked with an expiration date. You probably keep your orange juice or apple juice in a closed container in the refrigerator. Do refrigeration and a closed container help maintain the vitamin-C content? Design an experiment to determine if the vitamin-C content of orange juice changes after the expiration date or if proper storage is not available.

2. Like all nutrients, vitamin C has to survive the highly acidic environment of the stomach before it can be made available to the body. Design an experiment to determine if vitamin C is affected by stomach acid.

Design Your Own
Lab 7

What substances or solutions act as buffers?

Organisms and individual cells must keep an internal balance, known as homeostasis. There are many external factors that can cause an individual cell or entire organism to stray from this balance. For example, many of the metabolic activities of living tissues can alter the pH in a system. Life depends on maintaining an optimal pH range. Buffers are substances that release or accept hydrogen ions to keep the pH relatively constant. Our bodies contain natural buffers. In this laboratory exercise, you will design an experiment to determine which of several living tissues has the greatest ability to buffer a solution.

Problem
Design an experiment that will test the buffering power of several animal or plant tissue solutions.

Objectives
- Form a hypothesis about the success of certain materials as buffers.
- Design an experiment to test your hypothesis.
- Control the variables in your experiments.
- Draw conclusions about the success of animal and plant solutions as buffers in biological systems.

Safety Precautions
🥽 🧤 🧹 🚫 🔬 ☣

WARNING: *The HCl and NaOH can irritate the skin.*

Possible Materials
pH meter
stirring rod
50-mL beaker
500-mL beaker
50-mL graduated cylinder
0.1M HCl
0.1M NaOH
liver solution
egg solution
gelatin solution
fruit solution
cucumber solution
buffer 7
water

Hypothesis
Use what you know about buffers and the ability of substances to act as buffers to write a hypothesis. Indicate which material will act as the best buffer and why and how this compares with the buffering ability of water.

_____

_____

_____

_____

Plan the Experiment

1. Read and complete the lab safety form.
2. Choose four solutions to test for their ability to buffer substances in a living system. Be sure to test the solutions you listed in your hypothesis.
3. Decide on a procedure for testing your solutions. In the space provided below, write your procedure for testing the solutions. Include a list of the materials you will use.
4. Identify the independent variable, dependent variable, constants, and control group.
5. Decide how you will record your data and when you will record it. Design a data table to collect information about the number of drops of HCl added and the number of drops of NaOH added to a solution as well as a space for the pH of the solutions.

Check the Plan

1. Be sure that a control group is included in your experiment and that the experimental groups vary in only one way.
2. Make sure your teacher has approved your experimental plan before you proceed.
3. When you have completed your experiment, dispose of materials as directed by your teacher.
4. Wash your hands thoroughly with soap and water.

Record the Plan

In the space below, write your experimental procedure and make a sketch of your experimental design.

Laboratory Manual

Design Your Own **Lab 7, What substances or solutions act as buffers?** continued

Data and Observations

1. Use the space below to create a data table of your findings, including the pH of the solutions, the number of drops of HCl added, and the number of drops of NaOH added to the solution.

Analyze and Conclude

1. Of the solutions that you tested, which was the most effective buffer? Which was the least effective?

_____

_____

_____

2. What can you conclude about the buffering ability of water?

_____

_____

_____

3. Were plant or animal solutions the best buffers? Why do you think this is the case? What evidence do you have about the effectiveness of plant and animal buffers? Explain.

_____

_____

_____

4. Describe the control in your experiment. What did the control show?

_____

_____

_____

5. Error Analysis What were some possible sources of error in your experiment?

_____

_____

_____

6. Exchange your procedure and data with another group in your class for peer review. What do their data indicate about the ability of different substances to be buffers?

_____

_____

_____

Write and Discuss

Write a short paragraph describing your findings and indicating whether or not they support your hypothesis. Discuss any questions your findings might have raised.

_____

_____

_____

_____

Inquiry Extensions

1. Human blood normally has a pH of about 7.4. What activities or conditions can change blood pH? Is it easy or difficult to change blood pH? Research diseases or conditions that can change the pH. Describe the symptoms and possible outcomes, and discuss the remedies for such issues. Report your findings to the class in the form of a public service announcement.

2. What are the buffering mechanisms used by the body to maintain proper pH? How do they work?

Classic
Lab 8

Why do cells divide?

When cells grow to a certain size, their rate of growth slows until they stop growing. At this point, they have reached their size limit. A cell that has reached its size limit divides into two smaller cells. In this lab, you will explore one of the factors that limit cell size: the relationship between the size of the cell—specifically, its surface area and volume—and how efficiently substances diffuse across its cell membrane.

Objectives
- Model cells of different sizes with agar cubes.
- Model the diffusion of materials across a cell membrane.
- Calculate the surface area-to-volume ratio for model cells.
- Form a hypothesis about how cell division affects a cell's ability to absorb materials.

Materials
agar
beaker
timer
calculator
plastic ruler
100 mL 0.1M solution of hydrochloric acid
kitchen knife
plastic spoons
paper towels

Safety Precautions

WARNING: *Use caution when handling hydrochloric acid.*

Procedure
Part A. Setting Up the Experiment
1. Read and complete the lab safety form.
2. Obtain a block of agar containing phenolphthalein from your teacher. Recall that phenolphthalein turns pink in the presence of a base. It will become colorless in an acid.
3. Use a ruler to measure and a kitchen knife to cut three blocks out of the agar. One should be 3 cm on each side, one should be 2 cm on each side, and one should be 1 cm on each side.
4. **Figure 1** Place the three agar cubes inside the beaker. Cover with 100 mL dilute hydrochloric acid solution.

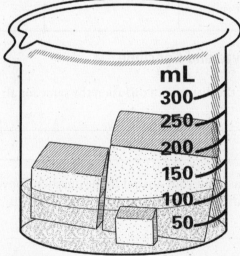

Figure 1

5. Leave the agar blocks in the dilute hydrochloric acid for a total of 10 min. Use a spoon to turn them every few minutes to ensure that they are soaking evenly.
6. Complete the data table on the next page.

Part B. Measuring Diffusion

1. After 10 min, carefully use the plastic spoons to remove the agar blocks. Blot them dry with paper towels. Use care not to splash HC1 on skin; it will cause burns.

2. Use the edge of the plastic ruler to cut each block in half. Measure the depth of the uncolored area in centimeters, recording the measurement to the nearest millimeter. This shows the depth of diffusion. Record these values in **Table 1.**

3. Complete **Table 1,** and answer the questions that follow.

4. You might need the following formulas:
surface area = length × width × number of surfaces
volume of a cube = length × width × height
Use a calculator for your calculations if necessary.

5. Wash your hands with soap and water, and dispose of the materials as instructed by your teacher.

Data and Observations

Table 1

Agar Data				
Cube Size	Surface Area	Volume	Ratio	Depth of Diffusion
3 cm/side				
2 cm/side				
1 cm/side				

Analyze and Conclude

1. Is the distance of diffusion the same for all of the blocks? Explain.

_____

_____

2. Based on your answer to the question above, do you think that the depth of diffusion is the same in all cells? Explain.

_____

_____

3. List the agar cubes in order of size, from largest to smallest. Then list them in order of surface area-to-volume ratio (from largest ratio to smallest ratio). How do these lists compare?

_____

_____

_____

Classic **Lab 8, Why do cells divide?** continued

4. Suppose you were given a microscopic, cube-shaped onion cell that was 0.01 cm/side. What would be the surface area-to-volume ratio of that cube?

_____

_____

5. Which block has the greatest surface area-to-volume ratio—the onion cube or the 3 cm/side cube you used in this lab?

_____

_____

6. What is the relationship between surface area-to-volume ratio and diffusion across a cell?

_____

_____

7. What happens to diffusion as a cell grows?

_____

_____

_____

8. **Error Analysis** What are some possible sources of error in your experiment?

_____

_____

_____

9. Form a hypothesis to explain how cell division affects a cell's ability to absorb the material necessary for growth. Base your answer on your observations of the surface area-to-volume ratio.

_____

_____

_____

Inquiry Extensions

1. Which cells in the human body divide most frequently? Why is this? What activities or conditions spur cell division? What slows it down?

2. During adolescence the human body grows at a rate faster than at any other time after infancy. Explain how what you learned in this lab plays out in the human body during adolescence.

Design Your Own
Lab 9

How many calories do different foods contain?

As you know, energy is stored in the bonds of large molecules. This means that chemicals in gasoline, natural gas, and food are forms of stored energy. Molecules of oxygen can break up the large molecules, releasing the energy. If this release of energy occurs quickly, it is called combustion (like the process that occurs in a car engine).

In your cells, the burning of food (glucose) occurs more slowly, which means that the energy is released more slowly. Some athletes, such as long-distance runners, take advantage of this phenomenon by eating large amounts of pasta the night before a race. The energy from the carbohydrate-rich food usually takes about a day to be released. Enzymes guide every step of this cellular respiration process so that the reaction does not happen all at the same time in an explosive fashion.

Energy is measured in calories. One calorie is the amount of energy needed to raise 1 mL of water 1° C. The measurement used on nutrition labels is **Calorie**, which equals 1000 calories. Calculate the number of calories using the following formula:

Number of calories = number of degrees the temperature rises × volume of water

Calculate the number of calories per gram using the following formula:

Number of calories ÷ gram = number of calories ÷ mass change

Problem
Determine the amount of calories per gram contained in different types of food. Identify which foods provide the most energy.

Objectives
- Identify foods to test.
- Assemble a simple calorimeter.
- Design an experiment to test a hypothesis.
- Draw conclusions about available energy in food.

Safety Precautions

WARNING: *Use care when touching hot metal. Be careful with pins and dissecting probe—they can pierce the skin.*

Possible Materials
metal coffee can (clean)
metal soup can (clean)
cork
straight pins or dissecting pins
aluminum foil
test-tube holder
graduated cylinder
masking tape
scale
food samples such as rice cakes, peanuts,
    dried beans, dried cheese, marshmallows
temperature probe or thermometer (non-mercury)
matches
candles
locking tongs
dissecting probe
weigh boats

Hypothesis
Use what you know about fats, calories, and foods in general to write a hypothesis indicating which types of foods have the greatest amounts of calories.

_____

_____

_____

Plan the Experiment

1. Read and complete the lab safety form.
2. Choose two different foods to test. Be sure to test the food you mentioned in your hypothesis.
3. Decide on a procedure for determining the calories in the food. In the space provided, write the procedure, including a list of materials you will use.
4. Identify the independent and dependent variables, the constants, and the control group in your experiment.
5. Decide how you will record your data. Consider gathering temperature information every 20 s. Design a data table to collect information about the beginning weight, end weight, water volume, and changes in temperature. Leave space in your data table for the calories.

Check the Plan

1. Be sure that a control group is included in your experiment and that the experimental group varies in only one way.
2. Make sure your teacher has approved your design and your experimental plan before you proceed.
3. When you have completed the experiment, dispose of the materials as instructed by your teacher.

Record the Plan

In the space below, write your experimental procedure and make a sketch of your experimental setup.

Design Your Own **Lab 9, How many calories do different foods contain?** continued

Data and Observations

1. Use the space below to create a data table of your findings.

Analyze and Conclude

1. Which food had the highest number of calories? Which food had the least?

_____

_____

_____

2. What does the data tell you about the energy the body can get from each of these foods? Explain.

_____

_____

_____

3. Why do you think there were differences in the calories of the foods?

_____

_____

_____

4. Use what you learned to write a definition for cellular energy, in your own words.

_____

_____

_____

5. Did all the food energy go into the water? Explain.

_____

_____

_____

6. Error Analysis What were some possible sources of error in your experiment?

_____

_____

_____

7. What is the primary difference between the form in which most plants store energy and the form in which animals store energy? How does each method benefit that type of organism?

_____

_____

_____

Write and Discuss

Write a short paragraph describing your findings and indicating whether or not they support your hypothesis. Discuss any questions your results might have raised.

_____

_____

_____

_____

Inquiry Extensions

1. Some cells are able to obtain energy from food without using oxygen. These organisms obtain their energy through fermentation, an energy-releasing process that does not require oxygen. Yeast is one such organism. Design an experiment to examine one factor that might impact the rate of fermentation.

2. Inorganic and organic fuels also release energy when burned. Design an experiment that will compare the amount of energy released by several types of fuel. For example, you might want to compare the calories that are released when burning different types of wood (hardwood v. soft wood), or the amount of energy released with the burning of different types of coal (lignite, bituminous, anthracite). When you have completed your experiment, draft a declaration on the environmental impact these fuels will have.

Design Your Own
Lab 10

What can affect the rate of photosynthesis?

Green plants can turn inorganic chemicals into organic food (stored energy). By synthesizing macromolecules, photosynthetic organisms transform nonliving materials into the building blocks of life. Plants take in water and carbon dioxide and make food through the process of photosynthesis. Light energy and chlorophyll are needed for this conversion. The amount of light a plant receives changes on a daily, weekly, and monthly basis.

Oxygen is a by-product of photosynthesis. The change in light intensity will probably impact the amount of oxygen a plant will produce. In this laboratory exercise, you will design an experiment that examines how light intensity impacts the rate of photosynthesis.

Problem
Determine how the intensity of light impacts the rate of photosynthesis.

Objectives
- Formulate a hypothesis about the connection between light intensity and oxygen production in photosynthesis.
- Design an experiment to test this hypothesis.
- Control variables, and use a control during your experiments.
- Draw a conclusion about the rate of photosynthesis.

Safety Precautions

Possible Materials
large glass jars (3)
aged tap water
baking soda (sodium bicarbonate)
scale
Elodea samples
ruler
scissors
small glass funnels (3)
test tubes (3)
lamp
medium to large box lined with white paper
medium to large box lined with gray paper

Hypothesis
Use what you know about photosynthesis to develop a hypothesis about the impact light intensity can have on the rate of photosynthesis.

_____

_____

_____

_____

Plan the Experiment

1. Read and complete the lab safety form.
2. Make a list of the impacts light might have on the rate of photosynthesis. Be sure to include the impacts you listed in your hypothesis.
3. Decide on a procedure for testing your hypothesis. In the space provided, write your procedure. Include a list of the materials you will use.
4. Identify the independent variable, dependent variable, constants, and control group.
5. Decide how you will record your data and when you will record it. Design a data table to collect information about the amount of oxygen produced.

Check the Plan

1. Be sure that a control group is included in your experiment and that the experimental groups vary in only one way.
2. Make sure your teacher has approved your experimental plan before you proceed.
3. When you have completed your experiment, dispose of materials as directed by your teacher.

Record the Plan

In the space below, write your experimental procedure and make a sketch of your experimental setup.

Design Your Own **Lab 10, What can affect the rate of photosynthesis?** continued

Data and Observations

1. Use the space below to create a data table of your findings, including information about the amount of oxygen produced.

Analyze and Conclude

1. What evidence do you have that plants need light for photosynthesis?

   _____

   _____

2. Is oxygen given off during photosynthesis? What is your evidence?

   _____

   _____

   _____

3. What purpose did the sodium bicarbonate serve?

   _____

   _____

4. What impact does light intensity have on photosynthesis? Make a general statement that explains your results.

_____

_____

_____

5. Describe the control in your experiment. What did your control show?

_____

_____

6. **Error Analysis** What were some possible sources of error in your experiment?

_____

_____

_____

7. Exchange your procedure and data with another group in your class for peer review. What do their data indicate about the impact light intensity has on photosynthesis?

_____

_____

_____

Write and Discuss

Write a short paragraph describing your findings and indicating whether or not they support your hypothesis. Discuss any questions your results might have raised.

_____

_____

_____

_____

Inquiry Extensions

1. Does the daily cycle of day and night impact a plant's overall rate of photosynthesis? Design an experiment that examines the changes in the release of oxygen between day and night. Then discuss how house plants or conifers might respond to seasonal changes and changes in the length of the day over the course of a year.

2. Why is it important to know about the production of oxygen by plants? What would happen to life on Earth if all plants disappeared? Now that you have seen how much oxygen a single plant can produce in a single day, research the total amount of oxygen in the atmosphere, the amount of oxygen needed to support life as we know it, and the approximate percentage of plants v. animal life on Earth. Use this information to create a time line that shows what would happen if there were no plants. Illustrate your time line with diagrams, and predict what changes would occur.

Classic
Lab 11

How long does each phase of the cell cycle last?

Have you ever considered what happens to you when you have an injury or you are in the middle of a growth spurt? What exactly is going on at the cellular level? Whether you are injured or you are growing, cells are busy growing and dividing during their cell cycle. During this investigation, you will be exploring each phase of the cell cycle by asking questions such as "What happens in each phase?" and "How long does each phase last?"

The cell cycle has a series of phases: interphase (which includes two growth phases and a DNA synthesis phase), mitosis, and cytokinesis. Mitosis can be broken into four different stages: prophase, metaphase, anaphase, and telophase. Each of these phases takes a different amount of time.

In this lab, you will be examining onion root cells under a microscope. You will find that different cells of the onion are at different stages in the cell cycle. Your job will be to count the number of cells representing each phase of the cell cycle. The cell cycle for onion root tips is about 24 h (or 1440 min). You will use the number of cells engaged in each phase as an indicator of how much time the cell spends in that phase.

Objectives
- Use a microscope to identify cells in an onion root tip.
- Identify the different stages of the cell cycle in onion cells.
- Count the number of cells in each stage of the cell cycle.
- Calculate the amount of time cells spend in each stage of the cell cycle.

Materials
microscope
colored pencils
calculator
prepared slide of onion root tip cells undergoing cell division

Safety Precautions

Procedure

1. Read and complete the lab safety form.
2. Familiarize yourself with the stages of the cell cycle. Sketch out the phases of cell division to help you identify those stages when you see them under a microscope.
3. Work with a partner and set up your microscope. One partner will act as the Observer and use the microscope to locate onion cells. The second partner will act as the Recorder and will tally the stages as the Observer calls them out.
4. Obtain a prepared onion root tip slide from your teacher and focus on it under low power.
5. Wait for instructions from your teacher. You will be timed during your observation of this onion cell.
6. Switch to high power and locate the region of active growth, just above the root cap.
7. The Observer should start with one long column of cells on the left side of the field of view. Identify the stage of mitosis that the cell is in. Call out the stage to your partner. Complete five to seven columns of cells. Then switch jobs with your partner.

8. The Recorder uses tally marks (in sets of five) to record the stages in **Table 1** as the partner calls them out.
9. Total the number of cells you find of each type. Put that number in the *Your Total* column of **Table 1**.
10. Wait until all your classmates have finished, and place their data (including your own) in the *Class Total* column of **Table 1**.
11. Calculate the percentage of each stage. Record this information in **Table 1**.
12. Assuming it takes 24 h for a cell to complete the cell cycle, calculate how long each stage takes (in hours). Hint: You will need to use your percentages for this calculation. Record your answers in **Table 1**.

Data and Observations

Table 1

Cell Cycle Data							
Stage	Description	Tally Marks	Your Total	Class Total	Total	Percent of Total	Time of Stage
Interphase							
Prophase							
Metaphase							
Anaphase							
Telophase							

Classic **Lab** 11, **How long does each phase of the cell cycle last?** continued

Data and Observations continued

1. In the space below, sketch and label an example of each stage of the cell cycle you observed.

Analyze and Conclude

1. Which stage of the cell cycle did you observe most often?

_____

_____

_____

2. What process must take place before mitosis can begin?

_____

_____

_____

3. Why might each stage of mitosis last a different amount of time? Explain.

_____

_____

_____

4. What can you infer about the relative length of time that each stage lasts?

    _____

    _____

    _____

5. What marks the completion of telophase? Describe any structures that you saw that indicate the end of that phase.

    _____

    _____

    _____

6. **Error Analysis** What are possible sources of error in your experiment?

    _____

    _____

    _____

7. Explain how the cell cycle can be described as multiplying by dividing.

    _____

    _____

    _____

Inquiry Extensions

1. Interphase and mitosis are similar in plant and animal cells, except that the centrioles appear during prophase in animal cells. Predict whether animal cells or plant cells spend a longer time in mitosis. Design an experiment to test your prediction.

2. Why is it important for you to think about mitosis and consider the amount of time cells spend in each phase? What does the cell cycle have to do with your life?

Design Your Own
Lab 12
Green or yellow?

The phenotype of an individual organism depends on both the environment and genes. A tree's genotype does not change, but the size, shape, and greenness of the leaves will vary depending on the amount of sunlight and wind. Environmental factors such as temperature, nutrition, exercise, and exposure to sunlight can influence the phenotype of an organism.

The product of a genotype is generally not a single, rigidly defined phenotype, but a range of possibilities influenced by the environment. For instance, most people have muscles (as determined by the genotype), but people who lift heavy weights often show larger, stronger, and better-defined muscles (the expression of the phenotype) than people who do not do strength training.

Many plants that are sold commercially come with tags specifying the best light conditions for healthy growth and the best display of foliage or flowers. This is an example of knowing what environmental conditions will affect the expression of phenotypes.

Problem
Design an experiment to examine the impact that exposure to sunlight has on the phenotypes of flowering tobacco seedlings.

Objectives
- Develop a hypothesis to predict the impact sunlight will have on the phenotypes of flowering tobacco seedlings.
- Design an experiment to test this hypothesis.
- Identify a control in the experiment.
- Draw conclusions from the plants that grow.

Safety Precautions
WARNING: *Be aware of mold growth on wet filter paper or seeds. Discard if mold is present.*
Be sure to wipe up any water that spills on the floor to prevent slips and falls.

Possible Materials
Nicotiana alata (flowering tobacco) seeds
filter paper
petri dishes
fine-point permanent marker
water
sunny spot in the room
dark corner in the room
metric ruler

Hypothesis
Use what you know about genetics to develop a hypothesis that will explain how sunlight impacts the phenotypes of a *Nicotiana alata* (flowering tobacco) plant, including the height or color of the seedlings, or number and quality of their leaves.

_____

_____

_____

_____

Plan the Experiment

1. Read and complete the lab safety form.
2. Choose the locations and the conditions in which you want to grow your *Nicotiana* seedlings.
3. Identify the independent variable, dependent variable, constants, and control group.
4. Decide how you will record your data and when you will record it. Design a table to collect information about the location of your samples and the growth, or lack of growth, that you observe.

Check the Plan

1. Make sure your teacher has approved your experimental plan before you proceed.
2. Be sure that a control group is included in your experiment and that the experimental groups vary in only one way.
3. Observe the growth of the seedlings in the different locations.
4. When you have completed the experiment, dispose of your seedlings as directed by your teacher.

Record the Plan

In the space provided, write your experimental procedure and make a sketch of the experimental setup.

Design Your Own **Lab** 12, **Green or yellow?** continued

Data and Observations

1. In the space below, make detailed drawings of your *Nicotiana* seeds as they grow. Be sure to make quantitative measurements.

2. Use the space below to create a data table for your findings, including the location of the seeds and the resulting color of the seedlings.

Analyze and Conclude

1. Of the seedlings that were grown in the dark, what was the ratio of green to yellow? What was the ratio of green to yellow for plants that were grown in the sunlight?

_____

_____

_____

2. Based on your observations, does environment have an impact on the phenotype of these plants? Which environmental factor in particular?

_____

_____

_____

3. Why do you think there were differences?

_____

_____

_____

4. Describe the control in your experiment. What did the control show?

_____

_____

_____

5. Error Analysis What were some possible sources of error in your experiment?

_____

_____

_____

6. Exchange your procedure and data with another group in your class for peer review. What do their data indicate about the seedlings' phenotypes?

_____

_____

_____

Write and Discuss

Write a short paragraph describing your findings and indicating whether or not they support your hypothesis. Discuss any questions your results might have raised.

_____

_____

_____

_____

Inquiry Extensions

1. Do other environmental conditions influence the phenotypes of tobacco seedlings? Choose another environmental factor to study, and design an experiment to test if that factor influences the phenotype.

2. Did you notice any differences between your experimental group and the control group that you did not anticipate? Make further comparisons between the two groups, and assemble the quantitative data. Design an experiment or conduct research to explore some of those unanticipated outcomes.

Classic
Lab 13

What are the chances?

Genetic disorders are abnormal conditions that are inherited through genes or chromosomes. Some genetic disorders are caused by mutations in the DNA of genes. Others are caused by changes in the overall structure or number of chromosomes.

Cystic fibrosis is a genetic disorder in which the body produces unusually thick mucus in the lungs and intestines. This makes it difficult for a person with cystic fibrosis to breathe or digest food. Cystic fibrosis is caused by a recessive allele. At this time, the symptoms of cystic fibrosis can be controlled, but there is no cure for this disease.

In this lab, you will determine the probability that cystic fibrosis will appear in the children of a couple who carry the traits for the disease.

Objectives
- Construct a pedigree for a family.
- Determine the probability of a couple having a child with the genetic disorder.

Materials
index cards (two colors—blue and pink)
scissors
pencil

Safety Precautions

WARNING: *Be careful when using scissors—they are sharp and can pierce or cut the skin.*

Procedure
1. Read and complete the lab safety form.
2. Read the following family history:

   Anthony and Emma have a daughter named Kathryn. Kathryn has been diagnosed with cystic fibrosis. Anthony and Emma are both healthy. Anthony's parents are both healthy. Emma's parents are both healthy. Anthony has a brother, named Corbin, who has cystic fibrosis.

3. In the space in the *Data and Observations* section, draw a pedigree that shows all the family members mentioned here. Use circles to represent the females and squares to represent the males. Shade the circles or squares representing the people who currently have cystic fibrosis.

4. Use the index cards to create a set of cards to represent the alleles. Cut three index cards of each color into fourths. On the 12 blue cards, write *F* to represent the dominant normal allele. On the 12 pink cards, write *f* for the recessive allele.

5. Use the cards to represent Kathryn's alleles. Write her genotype next to the pedigree symbol for Kathryn.

6. Use the cards to show Corbin's alleles and write the genotype next to his symbol.

7. Use the cards to determine what genotypes Anthony and Emma must have. Write their genotypes next to their pedigree symbol.

8. Use the index cards to determine the genotypes of the other family members. Fill in each person's genotype next to their symbol in the pedigree. Write in all possible genotypes.

Data and Observations

1. Use this space to draw a pedigree of Anthony and Emma's family.

Classic **Lab 13, What are the chances?** continued

Analyze and Conclude

1. What were the genotypes of Anthony's parents? What were the genotypes of Emma's parents?

_____

_____

_____

2. Anthony also has a sister, Zoë. What is the probability that she has cystic fibrosis? Explain.

_____

_____

_____

_____

3. What is the probability that Anthony and Emma will have another child with cystic fibrosis?

_____

_____

_____

_____

4. Why is information about several generations of family members necessary to get a good idea about a hereditary condition? Explain.

_____

_____

_____

_____

_____

5. Do you think cystic fibrosis is a sex-linked genetic disorder? Explain.

_____

_____

_____

_____

6. Error Analysis What are some possible sources of error in an exercise like this one?

_____

_____

_____

_____

_____

Inquiry Extensions

1. Some genetic disorders are more common in certain ethnic groups. Select an ethnic group, research the prevalence of inherited diseases for that group, and create a fictional pedigree to illustrate transmission patterns. Provide additional information on the prevalence of the disease in other ethnic groups.

2. Some diseases or traits are sex-linked. Research one such disease or trait, and report on how it is transmitted and which individuals are affected. In addition, make a fictional pedigree to demonstrate how a sex-linked disease would appear in a family across generations.

Classic
Lab 14

What is DNA?

There are 6 billion bits of information coded by DNA in each of our nucleated cells (a bit is a measure of information). Each human cell contains 21 times the information that is found in a set of encyclopedias, which is thought to have about 280 million letters.

DNA can be extracted from any living thing. Deoxyribonucleic acid is the blueprint for life, and all living things contain DNA. In this lab, you will conduct an experiment to extract DNA from different sources or to extract it from the same source by using different protocols. You will then compare your yield of DNA with that of your classmates.

In this procedure, mechanical mashing helps break down the cell walls. Heating destroys enzymes that can shear the DNA into small pieces. The detergent dissolves the lipids in the cell membranes and nuclear envelope (just like grease is dissolved in soapy dishwater). Once the membranes are dissolved, the DNA is free and very soluble in water. The enzyme (meat tenderizer) cleans the proteins, which might cling to the DNA. When the alcohol is added, the DNA clumps together and precipitates at the water/ethanol interface because DNA is not soluble in ethanol.

Objectives

- Extract DNA from organic sources.
- Compare the amount of DNA yielded from different sources.
- Design experiments to compare different extraction protocols.

Materials

various sources of DNA
various types of alcohol
various detergents
various sources of enzymes
non-iodized salt
hot-water bath
ice bath
ice cubes
beakers (50-mL, 250-mL, or large test tubes)
paper plate
knife and fork
10-mL graduated cylinder
cheesecloth
funnel
stirring rod
blender
balance
filter paper
wire inoculating loop
thermometer

Safety Precautions

WARNING: *Keep the cover on the blender when it is in operation. Use caution with the hot water—it can burn. Use caution with alcohol—it is flammable and can irritate the skin.*

Procedure

Part A. Extracting the DNA

1. Read and complete the lab safety form.

2. Working in two teams of two, decide whether you will test different sources of DNA or if you will vary your extraction protocol by manipulating the variables in bold type below. Design your experiment so that one team is the control. Your teacher will provide you with options. Decide your question and hypothesis for the experiment. Record these in the *Data and Observations* section. Record your design criteria in **Table 1**.

3. Prepare 10 mL of chilled **ethyl alcohol**.

4. Prepare the DNA extraction solution. Dissolve 2 g of salt in 90 mL of water in a 250-mL beaker. Then add 10 mL of **detergent**. Stir gently so you do not generate many suds.

5. Prepare the **source of DNA**. Place the DNA source on a paper plate or piece of waxed paper. Use a fork (and knife if needed) to mash it thoroughly. Place 30 g of the mashed DNA source in the extraction solution.

6. Check the **temperature** of your hot-water bath; the ideal temperature is 60°C. Adjust as needed by adding ice cubes or increasing the heat source. Place the beaker with the DNA source and extraction solution into the hot-water bath. Incubate the solution for **12 min**. Stir occasionally to distribute the heat. The temperature of the bath must be maintained during this incubation period.

7. After the incubation period, **transfer the solution to a blender and pulse the blender three to five times**. Do not let the blender run—the solution will become too sudsy. Return the solution to the beaker, and place the blended material into an ice bath for 5 min.

8. Pour the cooled extraction solution into your filter system. (Filter setups can include a funnel and cheesecloth or similar materials.) Allow the liquid to filter until you have 20 mL of filtrate in the bottom of a 50-mL beaker or large test tube.

9. Add a pinch of **enzyme,** and gently stir.

Part B. Precipitating and Drying the DNA

1. Tilt the beaker or test tube, and slowly add the 10 mL of cold alcohol, allowing it to slide down the side of the vessel and form a layer on top of the extraction solution.

2. Place the extraction/alcohol solution so that you can observe what happens where the alcohol and filtrate layers meet. Record your observations.

3. Let the solution sit for 2 min without disturbing it. A white precipitate will form in the alcohol layer. This is DNA, and it will appear as slimy, white strands or clumps of material.

4. Set a piece of filter paper on the balance, and record its mass in **Table 1**.

5. Use a wire loop to collect all the DNA from the top alcohol layer. Place the DNA you collect on the filter paper, and spread it out as much as possible; it will dry more slowly if it is clumped.

6. Clean up your lab materials as directed by your teacher. Wash your hands with soap and water when you are done.

7. Let the DNA sit for 24 h or until it is absolutely dry. Calculate the mass of the DNA collected [(Mass of the filter paper + DNA) – (Mass of the filter paper before DNA) = Mass of the DNA].

Classic **Lab** 14, **What is DNA?** continued

Data and Observations

1. What question are you exploring?

_____

_____

_____

2. What is your hypothesis?

_____

_____

_____

Table 1

Source of DNA or Change in Protocol		Mass of Filter Paper	Mass of DNA + Filter Paper	Mass of DNA
Independent variable				
Control				

Analyze and Conclude

1. We cannot isolate most of the other molecules that make up living things as easily as we can the DNA. Why do you think this is so?

_____

_____

_____

2. Did the DNA you collected come out in clumps or strands? Explain why this might be.

_____

_____

_____

3. Calculate how many times to the Moon and back a human's DNA would reach if it were removed from each cell and each strand were laid end to end. Each human cell nucleus holds about 2 m of DNA, and a typical adult human is composed of 60 trillion cells. The distance from Earth to the Moon is 380,000 km.

_____

_____

_____

4. As part of the procedure, you denatured proteins. What are the two major roles of proteins in living things?

_____

_____

_____

5. What properties does the detergent possess that make this experiment possible?

_____

_____

_____

6. Think about the amount of material with which you started. Now think about the amount of material that might typically be found at a crime scene (for example, a single hair follicle or dried saliva on an envelope). How would the DNA extraction process change if you were working with such a small sample?

_____

_____

_____

7. **Error Analysis** What were possible sources of error in your procedure?

_____

_____

_____

Inquiry Extensions

1. Do different sources give different amounts of DNA? Do certain properties of substances make it possible to extract more DNA? Design an experiment to test your hypotheses.

2. Does the type of detergent used make a difference in the success of extracting DNA? Do powdered soaps work as well as liquid? What about shampoo? Design an experiment to test your hypotheses.

Classic
Lab 15

Who did it?

An individual's DNA forms a unique pattern of bands that can be used to identify the person. This unique banding pattern produced by fragments of your DNA is called DNA fingerprinting. (Interestingly, identical twins have unique fingerprints, but their DNA markers are exactly the same.) Genetic markers can help identify the differences between two DNA samples. Genetic markers are specific stretches of DNA that vary among individuals.

Scientists use polymerase chain reactions (PCR) and gel electrophoresis to make a DNA fingerprint. PCR allows many copies of a certain segment of DNA to be made without using living cells. PCR can make multiple copies of one particular segment from within a large length of DNA. The DNA fragments are then separated by gel electrophoresis. In this process, the molecules or portions of molecules are separated according to length.

These two techniques, when used together, allow law enforcement to gather the smallest amount of evidence at a crime scene. DNA gathered from a blood or hair sample at a crime scene can then be compared to DNA from a suspect's blood or saliva.

Objectives
- Use models to represent DNA fingerprints.
- Infer why DNA patterns differ between individuals.
- Draw conclusions about which suspect was present at a crime scene.

Materials
mock DNA fingerprint set
magnifying lens
ruler
Figure 1

Procedure
Part A. Identify a Pattern

1. Read and complete the lab safety form.

2. Obtain a set of suspect "DNA fingerprints" from your teacher. These might look familiar. They are the Universal Product Codes (UPC) from several common products. For the purpose of this lab, these bar codes will be used to model DNA fingerprints.

3. Also obtain an envelope labeled *Crime Scene Data*. Your job will be to determine which of the suspects left behind evidence at a crime scene.

4. Use a magnifying lens to examine the DNA fingerprints carefully. The suspect whose DNA fingerprint matches the sample from the crime lab will be the suspect who is arrested for the crime.

5. Once you have isolated a suspect, take your answer to your teacher for review. If you are correct, you will be able to move ahead to the next section.

Part B. Using DNA Evidence

1. **Figure 1** is an example of DNA patterns made by gel electrophoresis derived from a DNA database. A series of bank robberies took place in one town during the past four days. Your job will be to determine if the robberies were linked and if any of the suspects now in custody are the guilty parties.

2. The First National Bank was robbed at noon on Monday. The bank robber ran up to the drive-through window and demanded money. The robber made off with an unspecified amount of money but cut a finger smashing the surveillance camera. Police detectives analyzed the blood sample. The DNA sample is the sample shown in the first column in **Figure 1**. It is labeled *Bank 1*.

3. The Second National Bank was robbed at 11 A.M. on Tuesday. This time, the bank robber entered the bank and handed the teller a note for an unspecified amount of money. The teller handed over the money but kept the envelope. Luckily for detectives, the robber licked the envelope and left behind a DNA sample. This sample is in the second column of **Figure 1**. It is labeled *Bank 2*.

4. The Third National Bank was robbed at 10 A.M. on Wednesday. The robber demanded money and left without leaving any evidence at the teller's station. However, the robber had been chewing gum and, just before stepping up to the teller, dropped the gum in the trash barrel. Observant bank patrons alerted the police, and the gum was collected and analyzed. DNA was extracted, and this DNA sample is seen in the third column of **Figure 1**. It is labeled *Bank 3*.

5. The police have found three possible suspects, and the suspects have consented to give DNA samples.

6. Examine the DNA strands and see if any of the suspects should be arrested for the crime or crimes.

7. Record your conclusions in **Table 1,** and answer the questions that follow. Indicate in the table whether or not the DNA from each suspect was found at a crime scene. Use an X to indicate a positive match.

DNA Gel Electrophoresis

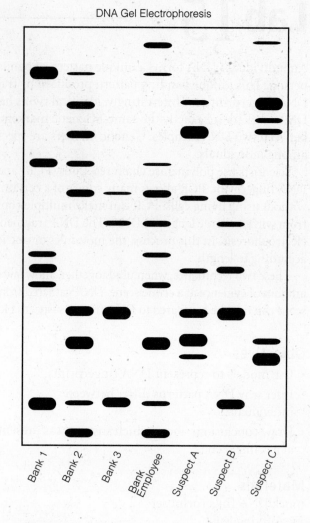

Figure 1

Classic **Lab 15, Who did it?** continued

Data and Observations
Table 1

DNA Data			
	Bank 1	**Bank 2**	**Bank 3**
Suspect A			
Suspect B			
Suspect C			

Analyze and Conclude

1. Were any of the three bank robberies committed by the same person? Explain how you know.

_____

_____

_____

_____

2. Is there a definite suspect for each bank robbery? Should any of the suspects be released? Do detectives need to gather more evidence in any of the cases? Explain.

_____

_____

_____

_____

3. Suppose detectives learn that Suspect A has an identical twin. How will this change their investigation?

_____

_____

_____

_____

_____

4. Error Analysis What sort of errors can occur when collecting and examining DNA samples?

_____

_____

_____

_____

5. How did the exercise where you examined UPC symbols compare with examining DNA fingerprints? How were the experiences similar or different?

_____

_____

_____

_____

6. Each suspect had a very different DNA fingerprint. Why do DNA fingerprints vary so much from person to person?

_____

_____

_____

_____

Inquiry Extensions

1. Suppose Suspect B is arrested for one of the bank robberies. You are his or her defense lawyer. Write a short paragraph stating why you plan to use the DNA evidence to help get your client acquitted.

2. Many criminal cases are solved using DNA evidence. Conduct research for a recent case which has been reopened or solved using DNA evidence. Report your findings to your classmates.

Classic
Lab 16

How do species compare?

In the 1740s, a French scientist first proposed the idea that all organisms are descended from a single common ancestor. **Figure 1** shows a widely accepted phylogenetic tree (an organizational chart) showing the relationships of major groups of animals. (The arrowhead on the left side of the chart points back toward the presumptive single ancestor.)

Scientists who have studied protein sequences have found evidence to support the idea of a common ancestor. They have determined that when two species share a similar sequence of protein chains, the species must have shared a common ancestor. The closer the sequences are to each other, the more recently the two species shared an ancestor. Numerous differences in the sequences indicate the two species are not as closely related.

For example, the amino acid sequence in the protein cytochrome c of humans exactly matches the sequence in chimpanzees. The human sequence differs only by one position when compared to that of a rhesus monkey. But for animals that we are clearly not closely related to, the sequence shows an even greater variance. The amino acid sequence of humans differs from that of a chicken by 18 positions and from a turtle's by 19 positions.

In this investigation, you will look at the amino acid sequences from a variety of organisms and discuss how closely related they are.

Objectives
- Examine a table of amino acid data.
- Interpret the table and find relationships.
- Draw conclusions about how closely related species are.

Material
copy of amino acid table

Procedure
Part A. Predict Relationships
1. Read and complete the lab safety form.
2. You will be using **Table 1** to examine amino acid sequences from the following animals: horses, donkeys, rabbits, snakes, turtles, and whales.
3. **Table 1** shows only a small segment of the sequence of amino acids within the cytochrome c protein. There are 104 amino acids in this protein. **Table 1** shows the sequence between positions 39 and 53.

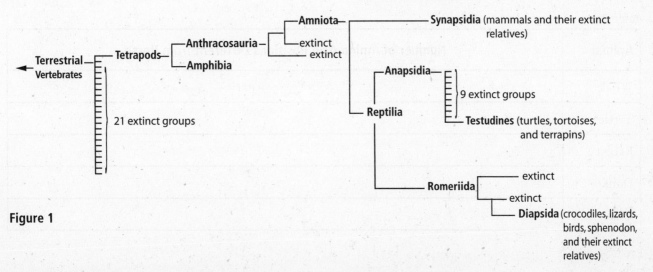

Figure 1

4. Use the characteristics of the animals, such as appearance, habitat, or diet, for example, to make a prediction as to which of them are most closely related. List these in the *Data and Observation* section of this lab.

5. Indicate which animals you think are the least closely related.

Part B. Examine Amino Acid Sequences

1. Compare the amino acid sequence of the horse to the rest of the animals. How many amino acids differ between the species? Record your results in the second column of **Table 2**.

2. Study the relationships between the species indicated in the first column of **Table 2**. What species shares the most similar sequence with a horse? Which species have sequences that are dissimilar?

Table 1

Position of the Amino Acids in Cytochrome c															
Position of the amino acid	**39**	**40**	**41**	**42**	**43**	**44**	**45**	**46**	**47**	**48**	**49**	**50**	**51**	**52**	**53**
Horse	A	B	C	D	E	F	G	H	I	J	K	L	M	N	O
Whale	A	B	C	D	E	Y	G	H	Z	J	K	L	M	N	O
Turtle	A	B	C	D	E	V	G	H	Z	J	K	U	M	N	O
Rabbit	A	B	C	D	E	Y	G	H	Z	J	K	L	M	N	O
Donkey	A	B	C	D	E	F	G	H	Z	J	K	L	M	N	O
Snake	A	B	C	D	E	Y	G	H	Z	J	K	W	M	N	O
Position of the amino acid	**39**	**40**	**41**	**42**	**43**	**44**	**45**	**46**	**47**	**48**	**49**	**50**	**51**	**52**	**53**

Table 2

Animal	Number of Amino Acid Positions Different from Horse
Whale	
Turtle	
Rabbit	
Donkey	
Snake	

Classic **Lab** 16, **How do species compare?** continued

Data and Observations

1. In the space below, construct a branching tree using this information. Your tree should include horses, donkeys, snakes, whales, turtles, and rabbits. Your tree should show one way that these species could have evolved from a common ancestor.

Analyze and Conclude

1. Which species are closest to a horse as indicated by the particular sequence of amino acids in **Table 1**?

_____

_____

2. Which species are more distantly related to a horse as indicated by the sequence of amino acids in **Table 1**?

_____

_____

_____

_____

3. Based on the evidence in **Table 2**, how would you describe species with similar amino acid sequences in terms of their shape and structure?

_____

_____

_____

4. Based on **Table 2**, make a general statement about whether any of the species other than horses are more or less similar to each other.

_____

_____

5. Based on the comparison you've made, rabbits and whales differ from horses by the same amount. What does this say about the relatedness of rabbits and whales? What might help you understand how those two animals are related? Explain your answers.

_____

_____

_____

6. If you compared the amino acid sequences in **Table 1** with those of another species, and found a different relationship between the species (for example, that snakes were closer to rabbits than to turtles) what conclusions might you draw?

_____

_____

7. **Error Analysis** What are possible sources of error in your experiment? How could you correct for them if you repeated the experiment?

_____

_____

_____

Inquiry Extensions

1. How would you compare the relatedness of all of the animals cited in **Table 1**? How closely related is each of the animals to all of the other animals? Would they change how you draw a branching tree for this group of species? If the data you compile in comparing all of the species seems contradictory (i.e., one species seems closer to another on one chart, but not on another), how would you resolve the contradiction? Would more data help, and if so, what kind of data?

2. What predictions could you make about amino acid sequences for species not shown in **Table 1**? Research amino acid sequences for cytochrome c for a new group of species. Compare the sequences using the same techniques as in this lab. Do your results support your prediction?

Classic
Lab 17

Could you beat natural selection?

Natural selection uses the principle of survival of the fittest. Fitness is often defined as the suitability of an organism to a given environment. It might be the case, however, that a certain set of features or characteristics that are favorable to an organism in one environment might prove to be unfavorable in a different environment. In some cases it might be true that altering the environment of an organism might decrease its chances of survival. In this lab, you will learn more about natural selection and survival of the fittest by deciding which characteristics are more favorable for survival in a variety of environments.

Objectives
- Locate organisms (represented by chips) in the natural environment of the classroom.
- Make a prediction about survivability of two sets of organisms.
- Simulate predator/prey relationships.
- Complete data tables.
- Graph results.

Materials
Part A
clear plastic chips
plastic chips in three additional colors
graph paper
colored pencils
calculator

Part B
one page of newspaper apartment rentals or stock quotes
sheet of plain paper, the same size as the newspaper
envelope of paper circles representing prey
forceps or pencil with eraser
stopwatch or watch with second hand
calculator

Procedure
Part A. Predator/Prey Relationships
1. Read and complete the lab safety form.
2. There are 100 plastic chips hidden around the room. You will have 3 min to search for them. Gather the ones that you find, and note the locations where they were found.
3. Stop after 3 min and count the number of chips that you found.
4. Work with your classmates to tabulate the total number of chips found by the class.
5. Complete **Table 1** showing the following information: original number of chips, color of chips, number of chips found by you, location found, number found by the rest of the class.
6. Use the graph paper to graph the results of the class with your data. In a bar graph, plot your data in one color and the class data in another.

Part B. Camouflage

1. Work with a partner. Decide which partner will be the predator and which will work with the prey (the "prey manager"). You must keep these roles throughout the exercise.

2. The predator hunts at twilight and in the early evening. The prey are the newsprint circles and the plain circles. These two sets of circles live in two different environments—newsprint paper and plain paper. The predator does not prefer one kind of circle over the other and simply feeds on any circles it come across.

3. With your partner, come up with a prediction explaining how the newsprint circle and the plain circle will be consumed or conserved. Write your prediction in the appropriate spot in the *Data and Observations* section.

4. The predator should wait in the hallway until called in by the prey manager.

5. **Figure 1** The prey manager should distribute both sets of circles randomly over the printed sheet of paper. This person needs to ensure that the circles are not piled up on each other and that they are distributed evenly over the paper.

6. When the prey has been distributed, the prey manager should bring in the predator. The predator should look at the paper and, using forceps or a pencil eraser, count how many circles of each type he or she can pick up in the span of 10 s. The prey manager should keep time.

7. After 10 s have passed, the predator should call out the number of newsprint circles and plain circles he or she picked up, and the prey manager should record these numbers in **Table 2**.

8. **Figure 2** The team should prepare for a second feeding. This time the predator should cover his or her eyes while the prey manager places both sets of circles on the plain paper. Again, count the number of circles the predator picks over the span of 10 s.

9. Repeat steps 4–8 two more times. Between each pair of trials, have the predator return to the hallway.

10. When the trials are finished, return the prey to the envelope and return all the supplies to your teacher.

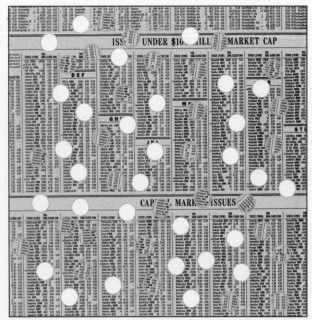

Figure 1

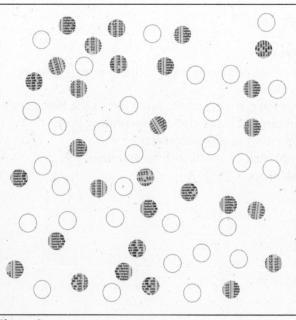

Figure 2

Classic **Lab** 17, **Could you beat natural selection?** continued

Data and Observations

Table 1

Chips Data

Chip	Original Number	Number Found by Me	Total Number Found	Number Left	Percentage of Chips Left
Clear					
Red					
Yellow					
Blue					

Prediction for Part B:

_____

_____

Table 2

Circles Data

	Plain Background		Newspaper Background	
	Plain Circles	Newsprint Circles	Plain Circles	Newsprint Circles
Total population				
	Number of Plain Circles Consumed	Number of Newsprint Circles Consumed	Number of Plain Circles Consumed	Number of Newsprint Circles Consumed
Trial 1				
Trial 2				
Trial 3				
Team average				
Percentage of circles that died				
Percentage of circles that survived				

Analyze and Conclude

1. Which of the four kinds of chips were most easily found?

_____

_____

2. Chips of which color were most difficult to find?

_____

_____

3. What environmental factors in the room allowed some protection for the chips?

_____

_____

4. Analyze which characteristics were favorable for these organisms and which characteristics made their survival less likely? Explain your answers.

_____

_____

_____

5. For Part B, how do the phenotypes of each species of circle affect the survival of the organisms?

_____

_____

_____

6. Error Analysis What are some possible sources of error in your experiment?

_____

_____

_____

7. After completing Part B of the laboratory, what can you conclude about the role of an organism's surroundings on its survival? Was this demonstrated by your experiences in Part A?

_____

_____

_____

Inquiry Extensions

1. This lab has shown a relationship between coloration and natural selection. What organisms use camouflage to increase their chances of survival? Create an electronic slide show to demonstrate and explain how these adaptations benefit the organism.

2. What other phenotypes (outward appearances) or physical characteristics contribute to an organism's survival? Given what you know about trends in environmental conditions, write a description of an adaptive characteristic that would benefit, during the next 100 years, an existing species that you encounter near your home.

Design Your Own
Lab 18

Does this animal walk on four legs or two?

Primates, early and present-day, have several characteristics in common. They share the ability to see in color and grasp with their five-digit hands, and the tendency to care for their young. Primates are divided into two groups, strepsirrhines/haplorhines anthropoids, a subgroup of the haplorhines Humans and apes are part of the anthropoid group. Evidence suggests that early hominoid anthropoids started walking on two legs about 4 million years ago.

In order for bipedalism to occur, several structural changes had to evolve. One of these is that the center of gravity of the hominid organism had to change in order for the body to be balanced in an upright position. A change in the position/shape of the pelvic bones to provide placement for upright walking muscles and support for inner organs was also needed. Finally, the position of the head on the spinal cord is changed. This allows the legs of biped organisms to be directly under the body to support the entire weight of the organism. In this laboratory exercise, you will design your own procedure for comparing the differences between animals that are bipedal and those that walk on four legs.

Problem
Paleoanthropologists need to determine if bone fragments come from an ape or a hominid.

Objectives
- Devise a plan to compare the limbs and pelvis of a gorilla, australopithecine, and present-day human.
- Make predictions about the differences between structures of bipedal and quadrupedal animals.
- Extrapolate the information gathered to a discussion on natural selection.
- Determine whether the australopithecines were habitual upright walkers (bipeds).

Safety Precautions

Possible Materials
calculator
human skeleton
diagram of pelvis and femurs of three animals
diagrams of gorilla, australopithecine, and human
scale drawing of human and gorilla on card stock
glue
scissors
ruler

Hypothesis
Study the diagrams of the human and the gorilla. Write several hypotheses about the bony structures, vertical lines of force, wear patterns, and center of gravity of each organism and how they are designed to best function in that organism.

_____

_____

_____

_____

Plan the Experiment

1. Read and complete the lab safety form.
2. Choose which parts of the body you will measure. Be sure to measure the body parts mentioned in your hypothesis.
3. Decide on your procedure for comparing the skeletons of humans and their early ancestors. In the space provided below, write your procedure for collecting this information. Include any materials you will use.
4. Devise a procedure for determining the center of gravity in each specimen.
5. Decide how you will record your data, and design a data table to hold this information.

Check the Plan

1. Make sure your teacher has approved your experimental plan before you proceed.

Record the Plan

Use the space below to write down your experimental procedure.

Design Your Own **Lab** 18, **Does this animal walk on four legs or two?** continued

Data and Observations

1. In the space below, create a data table of your findings.

Analyze and Conclude

1. Think about the gorilla, australopithecine, and human skeletons that you
compared. An animal with a center of gravity above and in front of the pelvis
has a tendency to fall over if standing on two legs. Which animal might have this
problem? What feature helps it compensate for this?

_____

_____

_____

_____

2. How is body weight distributed in a human? In a gorilla?

_____

_____

3. Based on what you have seen, do you anticipate that the australopithecine walked on two legs or on four? What information led to your conclusion?

_____

_____

_____

4. How might natural selection have caused the change from quadrupedalism to bipedalism?

_____

_____

_____

5. **Error Analysis** What are some possible sources of error in your measurements?

_____

_____

6. Exchange your plan and data with another group in your class for peer review. What do their data show about the comparisons between these three animals?

_____

_____

_____

Write and Discuss

Write a short paragraph describing your findings and indicating whether or not they support your hypothesis. Discuss any questions your results might have raised.

_____

_____

_____

_____

Inquiry Extensions

1. Scientists who are studying the reasons why human ancestors began walking upright are focusing on some key factors. Research and report on the hypotheses that are currently being explored. What evidence is there to support these hypotheses?

2. Create a family tree tracing the distant relatives of humans and how they have changed over time. Include a diagram of each relative, if possible, and a short paragraph about their distinguishing characteristics. Present your information to your class in the form of a poster or time line.

Classic
Lab 19

What is a taxonomic key?

Classification is a way of separating a large group of closely related organisms into smaller subgroups. The scientific names of organisms are based on the classification systems of living organisms. To identify an organism, a scientist might use a key. A key is a listing of characteristics, such as structure or behavior, organized so that an organism can be identified.

In this lab you will create a taxonomic key for the order Artiodactyla. Artiodactyls are mammals whose feet have an even number of toes, also known as paraxonic feet. Artiodactyls are primarily herbivores. This is a large and diverse group of mammals. There are approximately 220 living species of artiodactyls. Most live in open plains or savannas, but others live in forests, and some are semi-aquatic. Some of the fastest-running mammals are found in this order, but there are some that are slow and clumsy as well.

Paraxonic feet - order Artiodactyla   Modern Horse
                                                       single hoof

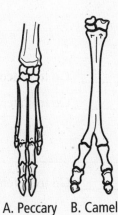 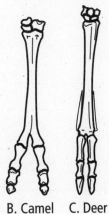 

A. Peccary   B. Camel   C. Deer   D. Hippopotamus   E. Pig   F. Elk   A. Horse

Figure 1

Objectives
- Use a key to identify common denominations of money.
- Examine the method used to make a key.
- Construct a key to identify a group of organisms.

Materials
set of coins (penny, nickel, dime, quarter) and bills ($1 and $5)
pen or pencil
reference material
animal envelope
index cards

Safety Precautions

Procedure
Part A. A Simple Taxonomic Key

1. Read and complete the lab safety form.
2. In the *Data and Observations* section you will find an unfinished taxonomic key for the money you have in front of you.
3. Fill in the missing information in the key, and pay attention to the way that the taxonomic key is set up and what sort of information is in it. You will be making your own taxonomic key in the next section.
4. Return all money to your teacher.
5. Wash your hands with soap and water after completing this part of the activity.

Classic **Lab** 19, **What is a taxonomic key?** continued

Part B. Making Your Own Taxonomic Key

1. Retrieve an animal envelope from your teacher.

2. Inside are pictures of ten animals belonging to order Artiodactyla. These animals are the even-toed ungulates. Ungulates are mammals with hooves, like horses. To see how even-toed ungulates differ from odd-toed ungulates like horses, see **Figure 1**.

3. Work with a partner to design a taxonomic key that will list the characteristics of these animals in a way that the organism can be identified.

4. Write down some characteristics of each animal. Pay attention to those characteristics that can distinguish one animal from another. Start with the most general characteristics and progress to increasingly more specific characteristics. Avoid using descriptors such as "large" or "small," if possible.

5. Write the characteristics you see on index cards. This will make them easier to manipulate and organize.

6. Determine which characteristic gives you the smallest number of subgroups. This is a good starting point for the key.

7. Determine how to break each subgroup into smaller subgroups, using pairs of characteristics (look back at the key for money). Keep working until you have separated all of your animals into their own groups. Start the choices in a pair with the same word, if possible. Start each couplet with different words, if possible.

8. Keep in mind that not everyone's key will be the same.

Data and Observations

1. **Taxonomic Key for Money**

   1A. Metal ....Go to statement 2

   1B. Paper ....Go to statement 5

   2A. Brown (copper) .... _____

   2B. Silver ....Go to statement 3

   3A. Smooth edge .... _____

   3B. Ridges around the edge ....Go to statement 4

   4A. Torch on back .... _____

   4B. Eagle on back .... _____

   5A. Number 1 in the corners .... _____

   5B. Number 5 in the corners .... _____

Classic **Lab 19, What is a taxonomic key?** continued

2. Taxonomic Key for Order Artiodactyla

1A. _____ .... _____

1B. _____ .... _____

2A. _____ .... _____

2B. _____ .... _____

3A. _____ .... _____

3B. _____ .... _____

4A. _____ .... _____

4B. _____ .... _____

5A. _____ .... _____

5B. _____ .... _____

6A. _____ .... _____

6B. _____ .... _____

7A. _____ .... _____

7B. _____ .... _____

8A. _____ .... _____

8B. _____ .... _____

9A. _____ .... _____

9B. _____ .... _____

10A. _____ .... _____

10B. _____ .... _____

Analyze and Conclude

1. What is a classification key, and how is it used?

_____

_____

2. List four different characteristics you used in your taxonomic key for the order Artiodactyla. Why did you choose these characteristics?

_____

_____

_____

_____

3. Which main characteristic could be used to distinguish a pronghorn sheep from a bushbuck?

_____

_____

4. Which main characteristic could be used to distinguish a mountain goat from a sheep?

_____

_____

5. Exchange your taxonomic key with that of another pair of students. Work through it to identify the animals. Is the key correct? How does your classmates' key differ from your own?

_____

_____

6. Error Analysis What are some possible sources of error in your taxonomic key? What information would have made it easier to overcome these issues?

_____

_____

_____

Inquiry Extensions

1. Choose another order, such as order Primate, and create a taxonomic key for several organisms in that order. Present your key to the class.

2. Walk around your neighborhood or school yard. Choose a category of items about which you can make a taxonomic key. This could be the types of trees or rocks, birds that live in or migrate through the area, or even vehicles in your neighborhood. Draw a detailed poster of the taxonomic key.

Laboratory Manual

Design Your Own

Lab 20

Can you filter out cholera?

In areas of southern Asia, such as Bangladesh, cholera is a common, and often deadly, disease. Copepods (miniature aquatic crustaceans) found in river water can carry a large number of *Vibrio cholera* bacteria in and on their bodies. When people drink untreated river water, the bacteria can produce a toxin that causes the small intestine to secrete massive amounts of fluid rich in salts and minerals, leading to dangerous bouts of diarrhea and dehydration. This disease is called cholera.

The river water can be sterilized by boiling, but this is not generally done because wood for fuel is scarce in Bangladesh and in many other developing countries. Tests have shown that filtering out the copepods can also remove much of the bacteria.

Recently, scientists and residents of Bangladesh have found that simple filters made of the cloth from women's saris can reduce the number of cholera cases by up to 50 percent. A sari is a traditional woman's garment made from a single rectangular piece of cloth measuring 5-6 m in length. It can be made from cotton, silk, or synthetic materials.

In this lab, you will use different types of fabrics to create your own water filter that could be used to clean the water in this area.

Problem
Test filters made of common cloth to see which will remove at least 25 percent of the copepods from river water.

Objectives
- Form a hypothesis about what type of filter would be the best to filter water containing copepods.
- Design a filter.
- Compare the number of copepods in a water sample before filtering to the number of copepods after filtering.

Safety Precautions

Possible Materials
simulated river-water sample
funnel
clean droppers (2)
large beaker
small beaker
graduated cylinder
microscope
slides with cell counter or slides with grids
cover slips
metric ruler
squares of cloth

Hypothesis
Use what you know about copepods, bacteria, and filters to write a hypothesis that will explain how to optimize copepod removal from a river sample.

_____

_____

_____

_____

Plan the Experiment

1. Read and complete the lab safety form.
2. Choose the material, or materials, you will use to make your filter.
3. Decide on a procedure for counting the copepods in the water before it is passed through the filter and after the water passes through the filter. Write your procedure for counting the copepods and setting up the experiment in the space provided below.
4. Identify the independent variable, dependent variable, constants, and control group.
5. Decide how you will record your data and when you will record it. Design a data table to hold your data and observations.

Check the Plan

1. Make sure the teacher has approved your experimental design before you begin. Make sure your personal safety equipment, including goggles, apron, and gloves, is in place before starting the experiment.
2. Be sure that a control group is included in your experiment and that the experimental group varies in only one way.
3. When you have completed the experiment, dispose of the simulated river water as directed by your teacher.
4. Wash your hands with soap and water.

Record the Plan

In the space below, write out your plan for testing the materials as filters. Sketch how you plan to set up the filters to allow the water to pass through.

Design Your Own **Lab** 20, **Can you filter out cholera?** continued

Data and Observations

1. Use the space below to create a data table of your findings.

Analyze and Conclude

1. Briefly explain your reasoning behind the construction of your filter.

_____

_____

_____

2. How well did your setup remove the copepods from the water? What was the percentage of difference in the number of copepods at the beginning of the experiment and the number at the end?

_____

_____

_____

3. What could be other benefits to using this type of filter? Explain.

_____

_____

_____

4. Describe the control in your experiment. What did the control show?

_____

_____

_____

5. Error Analysis What were some possible sources of error in your experiment?

_____

_____

_____

_____

6. Exchange your procedure and data with another group in your class for peer review. What do their data indicate?

_____

_____

_____

_____

Write and Discuss
Write a short paragraph describing your findings, and indicate whether or not they support your hypothesis.

_____

_____

_____

_____

Inquiry Extensions

1. Suppose your local water supply might be contaminated due to flooding. Design an experiment to determine whether the water is contaminated. Use the knowledge you have gained about filters. Show your design to the class.

2. The sari filters work well, but the procedure for making and using the filter needs to be distributed to everyone. Plan a public information campaign aimed at lowering cholera rates. Choose the best means of communicating, and decide what your main message will be.

Design Your Own

Lab 21

Do protists have good table manners?

Protists are eukaryotes that are not animals, plants, or fungi. Protists vary in structure and function more than any other group of organisms. Most protists are unicellular, although some, such as seaweed, are multicellular. Protists have organelles and a nucleus with a nuclear envelope.

Generally, protists are characterized by the types of food they consume and how they obtain it. Animal-like protists are heterotrophs that ingest food that they come across in the environment. Funguslike protozoans are also heterotrophs, but they eat mainly decaying organic matter. Plantlike protozoans are autotrophs and make their own food.

The manner in which protozoans eat also makes them unique. Some absorb food through their cell membranes. Others, like amoebas, surround food and engulf it. Others have openings called mouth pores into which they sweep food. In this lab, you will observe the eating techniques of paramecia—a type of protist.

Objectives

- Form a hypothesis about how environmental factors impact the eating habits of paramecia.
- Observe paramecia eating under a microscope.
- Identify a variable to test.
- Introduce an environmental variable, and record any changes in the paramecia's eating habits.

Safety Precautions

WARNING: *Use caution when handling slides—broken slides can cut skin. Be sure to keep lamps away from water sources to avoid shock.*

Possible Materials

microscope
slides and cover slips
eye droppers (2)
sample of pond water
yeast mixture
data table
table lamp
methyl cellulose or 3% gelatin solution
ice
plastic gloves
warm water (26°C to 30°C)
cold water (14°C to 18°C)
caffeine solution (1g/L)
sugar

Hypothesis

Use what you know about the movements and behaviors of paramecia to write a hypothesis indicating the impact of an environmental factor on the way paramecia consume their food.

_____

_____

_____

_____

Plan the Experiment

1. Read and complete the lab safety form.
2. Obtain a sample of pond water from your teacher.
3. Decide how you will identify specific paramecia to study and how much food you should give them. If the paramecia are moving too quickly for you to observe, slow them down by adding methyl cellulose or 3-percent gelatin solution to the water.
4. Decide which environmental factor you will change while you observe their eating habits.
5. Decide how you will observe the paramecia eating and how you will record your observations.
6. Discuss your plan with your classmates and teacher.
7. Try drawing what you see under the microscope. Design a data table to hold your observations.
8. Decide if there are other variables that could control the eating habits of paramecia. What roles do temperature, sunlight, the amount of food available, or competition from other paramecia play in determining how the organism eats? Choose a variable you want to test.
9. Identify the independent variable, dependent variable, constants, and control group for your new test, and record your data. Share your results with the class.

Check the Plan

1. Be sure that you have included a control group for the second part of the exercise.
2. Wear gloves when handling the culture.
3. Make sure your teacher has approved your procedure for the second part of the lab before you proceed.
4. Observe the behavior of a paramecium as it eats.
5. When you have completed the experiment, dispose of the pond water as directed by your teacher.

Record the Plan

In the space below, write your experimental procedure.

Design Your Own **Lab** 21, **Do protists have good table manners?** continued

Data and Observations

1. In the space below, make drawings to show what you saw through the microscope as the paramecia ate the yeast mixture. Include a labeled diagram of a paramecium in your response.

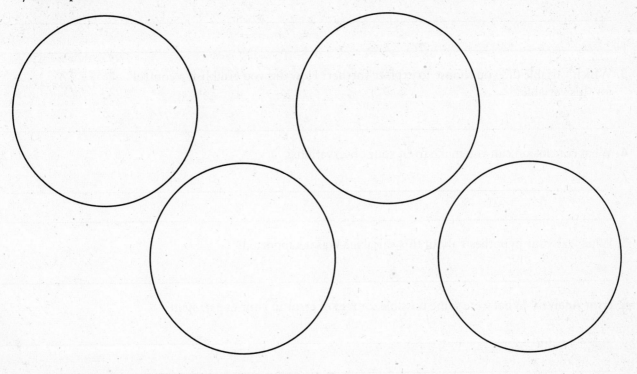

2. Use the space below to list the different behaviors that the paramecia of the test group exhibited as they ate.

3. Use the space below to explain how the behavior of the eating paramecia changed when one variable was changed.

Copyright © Glencoe/McGraw-Hill, a division of The McGraw-Hill Companies, Inc.

Analyze and Conclude

1. How do paramecia eat? Describe your observations.

_____

2. Based on your observations, what is the role of the cilia in the consumption of food?

_____

_____

3. Which variable did you choose to explore further? How did you establish a control for this variable?

_____

_____

4. What conclusion can you make from your observations?

_____

_____

5. What was your hypothesis about this variable? Was it supported?

_____

6. Error Analysis What were some possible sources of error in your experiment?

_____

_____

7. Share your conclusions and observations with your classmates. What inferences can be made about the optimum conditions for paramecia feeding?

_____

Write and Discuss

Write a short paragraph describing your findings and indicating whether or not they support your original hypothesis. Discuss any questions your results might have raised.

_____

_____

_____

Inquiry Extensions

1. How do other protists ingest food? If there are any differences in how food is ingested, how do you explain them? Observe other protists found in your pond water, and compare their methods of feeding with that of the paramecia.

2. Which do you eat more rapidly—french fries or carrots? Do paramecia change their eating habits with different food sources? Research different potential food sources for paramecia. Conduct the experiment again to see if you can observe changes in activity based on the presence of different food sources.

Classic
Lab 22

What are mushroom spores?

Mushrooms, such as those that are found in your yard or in the woods, are fungi. Fungi exist in a variety of sizes, ranging from a single cell of yeast to large, multicellular mushrooms. Fungi need moist, warm places to grow. All fungi, including mushrooms, are eukaryotes and heterotrophs, and they use spores to reproduce. In this lab, you will examine the characteristics of some common mushrooms and learn how they are spread.

Objectives
- Identify the parts of a variety of supermarket mushrooms.
- Learn about the spores of a mushroom by creating and examining a spore print.
- Determine how spores are spread by making a model from a balloon and cotton balls.

Materials
magnifying lens
mushrooms of different varieties purchased from local grocery store
dissecting probe
paper towels
white paper
large plastic container with lid
round balloon
cotton balls
tape
ruler or stiff stick
modeling clay
pin

Safety Precautions
WARNING: *Do not eat any of the mushrooms you are using in this laboratory.*

Procedure
Part A. Identify the parts of a mushroom.
1. Read and complete the lab safety form.
2. Obtain three mushroom samples from your teacher. Remember, do not eat anything given to you in a laboratory setting. Also, do not eat mushrooms you might find in the wild. Many could be poisonous.

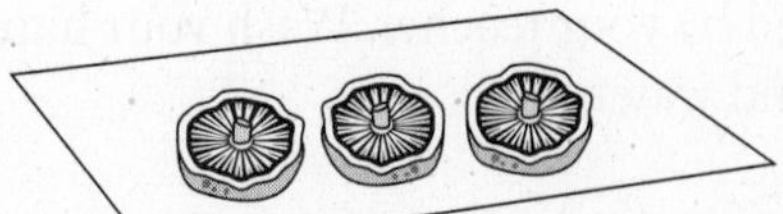

Figure 1

3. **Figure 1** Identify the different parts of each mushroom: the gills, cap, and stalk.
4. Twist off the cap of each mushroom and break open the stalks from end to end.
5. Draw detailed diagrams of each mushroom and label the individual parts of each one. Be sure to include a description of the threadlike structures within the stalk.
6. Dispose of the mushroom pieces as instructed by your teacher and wash your hands with soap and water.

Part B. Make A Spore Print
1. Obtain some mushrooms from your teacher. Gently twist the caps off of the mushrooms.
2. Remember: Do not eat the mushrooms provided in this lab.
3. Cut a piece of white paper to fit and place it inside the bottom of the plastic container.
4. **Figure 2** Place the mushroom cap, gill side down, on the paper and put the cover on. Place the container in an area of the classroom where it will remain undisturbed.

Figure 2

5. Wash your hands with soap and water.

6. After at least two days, carefully remove the top from the container and pick up the mushroom cap. You will find a spore print on the white paper.

7. Examine the spore print with your magnifying lens or a binocular scope if one is available. Draw a detailed diagram of your spore print, describing the relationship between the spores and the structures in the mushroom cap

8. Dispose of the print and mushroom cap as directed by your teacher. Wash your hands with soap and water.

Part C. Spore Dispersal

1. Now that you have seen what the spores of a mushroom look like and where they are stored, make a model of how spores are released into the air.

2. Assemble the materials that are needed for this model. These include the cotton balls, balloon, tape, ruler, clay, and pin.

3. Break a cotton ball into small pieces. Roll them into little balls.

4. Place each small cotton ball into the balloon. Continue until the balloon is about ¾ full.

5. Inflate the balloon, being careful not to inhale any of the cotton ball pieces. Tie off the end of the balloon with a knot.

6. Tape the knotted end of the balloon to the stick or ruler. Stand the stick up in the clay.

7. Make a drawing of your model. Be sure to label the parts of your model with the actual part of the mushroom that they represent.

8. Choose one group member to pop the balloon. The rest of the group members should stand back about one meter from the setup as that person pops the balloon with the pin. (Use caution: Pins are sharp and they can puncture skin.)

9. Observe what happens when the balloon pops.

Data and Observations

1. Use the space below to draw your observations from Part A of the investigation.

2. Use this space to draw your mushroom spore print.

Classic **Lab 22, What are mushroom spores?** continued

3. Use this space to draw and label your experimental design for spore dispersal and the results.

Analyze and Conclude

1. What are the threadlike structures inside the stalk of the mushroom? Of what are they made? Did every mushroom you examined contain them? Explain.

_____

_____

2. What function do you think these structures serve underground for the mushroom?

_____

_____

_____

3. Look again at the diagram you drew of your spore print. Based on what you saw in the print, how many spores do you think a mushroom could produce? Where do you think mushroom spores might be most likely to grow into new mushrooms? What do you think happens to the spores that do not grow into mushrooms?

_____

_____

_____

_____

4. Based on what you saw in your spore print, and in your model of spore dispersal, why do you think mushrooms are found just about anywhere?

_____

_____

_____

5. How did building a model help you understand the dispersal of mushroom spores better?

_____

_____

_____

_____

6. **Error Analysis** What are possible sources of error in your experiment?

_____

_____

_____

7. How might the addition of wind, in the form of a fan, affect the results of your spore dispersal model?

_____

_____

_____

_____

Inquiry Extensions

1. There are more than 3000 types of mushrooms in North America. Research one poisonous variety. Be sure to include a diagram of the major structures as well as hints as to how to identify it.

2. Mushrooms have a wide array of methods and mechanics for releasing spores. What are some of these methods? Besides wind, what other factors might aid in spore dispersal? What other kinds of dispersal methods do mushrooms use?

Laboratory Manual

Classic
Lab 23

How do ferns, mosses, and conifers reproduce?

Have you seen recent films or TV shows featuring computer-generated dinosaurs? The most accurate depictions show dinosaurs tramping through fern and pine forests and strolling over moss-covered ground. These types of plants were abundant during the Mesozoic era (248 to 65 million years ago).

The seeds, spores, and sperm of different types of plants vary widely in structure and function. In this laboratory experiment, you will examine the actual spores and seeds of a variety of plants and then examine diagrams of the life cycles of these plants. This information will be used to compare the life cycles of ferns, mosses, and conifers.

Ferns are seedless vascular plants. As you examine the fern fronds, you will notice small brown or black dots on the underside. These are spore capsules (sori). Mosses are nonvascular plants. They rely on osmosis and diffusion to transport water and nutrients from one part of the plant to another. Conifers are gymnosperms that produce both pollen and seeds.

Objectives

- Examine samples of ferns, mosses, and conifers.
- Compare characteristics of seeds, spores, and pollen in each.
- Infer how these characteristics have made survival of each plant possible.

Materials

fern fronds
moss sample
pine cones (male and female)
diagrams of the life cycles of ferns, mosses, and conifers
scalpel
forceps
paper towels
dropper
water
petri dish
magnifying lens
colored pencils

Safety Precautions

WARNING: *Use extreme care when handling the scalpel—it is very sharp and can easily cut or puncture the skin.*

Procedure

1. Read and complete the lab safety form.
2. Examine the diagram of the life cycle of each type of plant.
3. Obtain samples of a fern, moss, and pine cones. Examine each one closely, using the magnifying lens or stereomicroscopes if necessary. Make a detailed drawing of each in the *Data and Observations* section of this lab.
4. As you make your drawings, label the following as you see them: seeds, spores, sperm, ovaries, and pollen.
5. After completing your observations and drawings, identify one spore capsule on a fern frond and one seed from the pine cone. Isolate these and place each on a piece of paper towel. If your moss sample has well-developed sporophytes, you can examine spores of these as well.
6. Working carefully, use the scalpel to open either the seed, sporophyte, or spore capsule. Draw what you see. Notice the stage of development of each and make note of any other characteristics you see. Make a detailed drawing of each.
7. Clean up your lab station as directed by your teacher. Wash your hands with soap and water after handling the specimens.
8. Refer to your drawings when answering the questions that follow.

Data and Observations

1. In the space below, make detailed drawings of the fern frond, moss sample, and pine cone.

Fern Frond

Moss

Pine Cone

Classic **Lab 23, How do ferns, mosses, and conifers reproduce?** continued

2. In the space below, make detailed and labeled drawings of the spore capsule, moss sporophytes, and the conifer seed.

Spore Capsule

Moss Sporophytes

Conifer Seed

Analyze and Conclude

1. What features did you see on the fern frond?

_____

_____

2. What did you notice about the moss sample?

_____

_____

3. What features did you see in the pine cone?

_____

_____

4. What do the differences in the structures of these three plants tell you about the life cycle of each one?

_____

_____

5. How is a fern capsule different from a conifer seed? How are they similar? How does a moss sporophyte compare to the other two?

_____

_____

6. Error Analysis What were some possible sources of error in your analysis?

_____

_____

_____

7. What conclusions can you draw about the survival needs of each type of plant based on your observations?

_____

_____

_____

Inquiry Extensions

1. What structures in a moss plant make it possible for it to live on land? Explore a sample of moss in more depth, and design an experiment to examine the role moisture plays in the survival of mosses.

2. What role do these three kinds of plants play on Earth? What is their value in an ecosystem? What is their value to human beings?

Design Your Own
Lab 24

Do plants sweat?

Imagine that a catastrophic change in weather patterns caused a shift in air currents that has virtually eliminated rainfall over the rain forests of Costa Rica. Rainfall that was normally 37 cm per month has dropped to 5-10 cm per month, and coastal winds have increased. Now instead of a steady rain, plants depend solely on water that they receive from rivers and groundwater.

Water moves within the roots, stems, and leaves of a plant. Transpiration is the loss of water through leaves due to evaporation. Transpiration makes use of cohesive and adhesive forces on the water within the xylem to bring water from the ground and raise it through the trunk, branches, stems, and leaves. In this way, the plant can deliver water and dissolved nutrients to all of its parts and cool itself.

In one part of the rain forest, multiple streams and rivulets supply adequate water to the roots of trees and ground-hugging plants. It is also shaded for a good portion of the day and protected from winds by cliffs on three sides. Is there any chance that this area might begin to recapture the humid atmosphere of the old rain forest? You have been assigned to research how effectively the rain forest plants are adjusting, or not adjusting, to the new conditions.

Problem
Plants that used to be in a humid environment are now in a dry environment.

Objectives
- Form a hypothesis about how transpiration is affected by a change in an environmental condition.
- Design an experiment to test the impact of this environmental condition.

Safety Precautions
🥽 🧤 ✋ ♨ 💧

WARNING: *Keep fans away from water, and plug them into a GFI-protected circuit. Handle sharp scissors with care. Use only fresh plants—plants placed in water over several days will have bacterial or mold growth.*

Possible Materials
electric fan
food coloring
live plant
pipette
scissors
small beaker
small plastic bags (not the zippered kind)
ties
petroleum jelly
water

Hypothesis
Use what you know about transpiration to write a hypothesis that could explain which environmental factors affect the rate of transpiration in a plant.

_____

_____

_____

_____

Plan the Experiment

1. Read and complete the lab safety form.
2. Choose which environmental factor you will investigate. Transpiration rates can be influenced by humidity, the amount of light, wind, and other factors.
3. Decide on a procedure to use to test the impact that the environmental factor has on transpiration. You might have to observe your design over the course of several days. Record your procedure below. Include the materials you will use.
4. Identify the independent variable, dependent variable, constants, and control.
5. Sketch the experimental setup.
6. Design a data table to record environmental factors and information on the amount of transpiration. Include a time line describing the duration of the experiment and individual checkpoints.
7. The structure of a plant stem has a big impact on transpiration within the plant. Include a labeled diagram of the structure of the plant stems you are studying, and use this diagram to indicate the significance of the movement of water within the plant.

Check the Plan

1. Be sure that a control group is included in your experiment and that the experimental group differs in only one way.
2. Make sure your teacher has approved your experimental plan before you proceed.
3. Observe your experimental design for evidence of transpiration.
4. When you have completed the experiment, dispose of the plant cutting as directed by your teacher.

Record the Plan

In the space below, write your experimental procedure and make drawings of your experimental design. Be sure to indicate your control, the variables, and the constants in your design.

Design Your Own **Lab 24, Do plants sweat?** continued

Data and Observations

1. Use the space below to create a data table of your findings, including the location of the plants, the variables measured, and the transpiration observed.

Analyze and Conclude

1. Which environmental factor did you choose to examine in this experiment? Why did you choose this one?

_____

_____

_____

2. Based on your observations, how did your chosen environmental factor affect the rate of transpiration?

_____

_____

_____

3. What other factors do you think might affect the rate of transpiration in a plant? How might you test for those?

_____

_____

_____

4. Describe the control in your experiment. What did the control show?

_____

_____

_____

5. Error Analysis What were some possible sources of error in your experiment?

_____

_____

_____

_____

6. Exchange your procedure and data with another group in your class for peer review. What does their data show about transpiration in plants?

_____

_____

_____

_____

Write and Discuss
Write a short paragraph describing your findings and indicating whether or not they support your hypothesis. Did the environmental factor you studied affect transpiration? Discuss any questions your results might have raised.

_____

_____

_____

_____

_____

_____

Inquiry Extensions
1. Examine plants in your yard or in a local park. What environmental factors exist in these locations that could affect the rate of transpiration for these plants? Make a map of the area which shows the factors that could affect it.

2. In addition to water, humans secrete some chemicals that they have metabolized in their sweat. How would you determine if plants have the same ability? Conduct the experiment again to see if you can detect chemicals released during transpiration. Present your findings to the class.

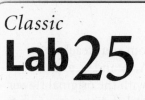

How does a flower grow?

Flowers come in many shapes and sizes, but they all perform the same function— reproduction. A flower is the reproductive structure of an angiosperm. Sepals, petals, stamens, and pistils are easily identifiable structures within a flower. In this lab, you will examine each of these carefully and determine how they relate to the overall function of the flower.

Objectives
- Dissect flowers to examine female and male parts.
- Measure and describe characteristics of flowers.
- Draw and label flower diagrams.
- Draw conclusions about reproduction in plants.

Materials
paper towels
dropper
magnifying lens
flower identification book (field guide)
microscope
slide
large flowers (2)
cover slip
scalpel
cellophane tape
water
metric ruler
lens paper
colored pencils

Safety Precautions

WARNING: *Be careful when using the scalpel. It is extremely sharp and can cut or pierce the skin.*

Procedure
Part A. The Visible Parts of the Flower
1. Read and complete the lab safety form.
2. Cover your work space with a few paper towels. Obtain a flower from your teacher (Flower 1).
3. Carefully examine the flower. Observe, measure, and record as many characteristics about your flower as possible. These could include the color of the petals, number of petals, distinguishing

marks, scent, and length of the petals and flowers. Record this information in **Table1**.
4. Create a sketch of your flower in the space provided on the next page, label the parts, and list your observations and measurements next to it. Take special care to notice the sepals and the relationship they have to the rest of the flower. Be sure to include these in your diagram.
5. Carefully pull away the sepals to expose the bases of the petals underneath. (If you have difficulty removing the sepals, you can use the scalpel to cut them away as long as you are careful not to damage the underlying structures.) Make special note on your diagram of the number of petals and any differences between different petals.

Part B. The Male Part of the Flower
1. Carefully pull off all the petals of the flower. This will expose the male parts of the flower.
2. Locate the stamens. Draw a diagram of what you see. Measure the length of each stamen, and indicate this on your diagram. Also include information on the number and shape of the stamens.
3. Use the scalpel and carefully cut the stamens away from the rest of the flower. Place these on your paper towel.
4. Obtain a clean microscope slide and cover slip. Gently tap some of the pollen grains from the anther onto the slide. Make a wet mount of the pollen.
5. Observe the pollen you collected at low power and high power under your microscope. Draw what you see under the microscope in the space provided in the next section. Be sure to indicate the magnification you are using.

Part C. The Female Part of the Flower

1. Carefully cut the pistil away from the rest of the flower using the scalpel. Write down as many measurements and descriptions of the pistil as possible. Include a diagram of the pistil with your explanation.
2. Check for other properties of the pistil. Check to see if the top of the pistil will pick up a piece of lens paper. Record your observations near your diagram.
3. Lay the pistil on the paper towel, and use the scalpel to carefully cut it in half. Draw a diagram of what you see, including the number of compartments and ovules.

Part D. Flower Comparisons

1. Obtain another flower from your teacher (Flower 2). Repeat steps A, B, and C, and compare the new flower with the original flower you examined. Draw and label diagrams of what you see.
2. Use the field guide to identify each flower.
3. Answer the questions in the *Analyze and Conclude* section.

Data and Observations
Table 1

Flower Data			
Part of the Flower	**Flower 1**	**Flower 2**	**Description**
Petals			
Sepals			
Stamens			
Pistil compartments			
Ovules			

Visible Parts of Flower 1
Male Parts

Female Parts

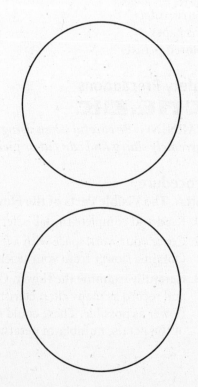

Classic **Lab 25, How does a flower grow?** continued

Visible Parts of Flower 2
Male Parts

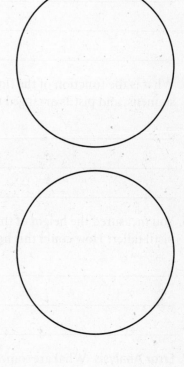

Female Parts

Analyze and Conclude

1. How do the sepals relate to the rest of the flower? What did you notice about the sepals of each of your flowers?

_____

_____

_____

2. Were all the petals on your flowers the same? Explain.

_____

_____

_____

3. Based on your observations, how would you describe the arrangement of the sepals, petals, stamens, and pistils in your flowers?

_____

_____

_____

_____

4. What was the relationship between the number of ovules, eggs, seeds, and ovaries in your flowers?

_____

_____

_____

5. What is the function of the flowers you observed? How are the sepals, petals, stamens, and pistils arranged to serve this function?

_____

_____

_____

6. You measured the height of the pistil and the stamens in each flower. Why is the pistil taller? How could this help you explain how this flower is pollinated?

_____

_____

_____

7. Error Analysis What are some possible sources of error in this experiment?

_____

_____

_____

_____

8. Were your flowers monocots or dicots? How do you know?

_____

_____

_____

Inquiry Extensions

1. How can the examination of a flower tell you anything about the plant from which it came? Use your observations from this lab to write a paragraph explaining the connection between flowers and plants.

2. Examine fruit provided by your teacher. Isolate the seeds and, if possible, dissect them to see the cotyledons. Using your knowledge of the growth habit of the parent plant and what you have seen of the fruit and seeds, make a prediction about the characteristics of the fruit's flower, methods of pollination, and seed dispersal. Follow up with research in the library. What role does the fruit perform? In its natural habitat, is the method of seed dispersal efficient and effective?

Classic
Lab 26

Is that symmetrical?

Some animals have bilateral symmetry. This means that a line can be drawn through the animal's body that divides the organism into two halves that are mirror images of each other, as shown in **Figure 1**. Nonliving objects such as spoons and eye-glasses have bilateral symmetry. Animals with radial symmetry have many lines of symmetry that pass through a central point, as shown in **Figure 2**. Bicycle wheels have radial symmetry.

The bodies of complex animals all have either bilateral or radial symmetry. In this lab, you will explore the symmetry found in some animals, create models, and investigate the symmetry of human faces.

Figure 1

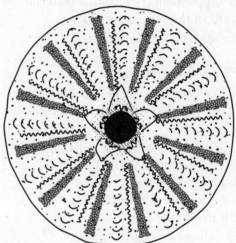

Figure 2

Objectives

- Identify lines of symmetry in animal samples.
- Model symmetry in the human face.
- Infer relationships between body structure and survival.

Safety Precautions

WARNING: *Handle the animal samples with care. Wash hands with soap and water after handling the specimens; preservatives can be toxic. Use caution when cutting the clay with the plastic knife.*

Materials

pencil
ruler
plain, unlined paper
selection of full facial portraits cut in half lengthwise
tracing paper
glue or rubber cement
cellophane tape
preserved sample or photograph of an animal
supplementary resource materials on each animal
   sample
modeling clay in two colors
plastic knife
small mirror

Procedure

Part A. Types of Symmetry

1. As you conduct your examination of each animal sample, record your observations in the appropriate cell of **Table 1**.

2. Examine each animal sample your teacher has set out. Identify the animal and which type of symmetry it has. Record this in **Table 1**.

3. In **Table 1**, draw a detailed diagram of the animal, indicating the line or lines of symmetry. Use the small mirror to ensure that your diagram is symmetrical.

4. Use any supplementary resource materials you have to fill in the rest of the chart.

5. Wash hands with soap and water.

Part B. Are faces symmetrical?

1. Work with a partner. Each of you should take one half of the same portrait and complete steps 2-6.

2. Fold the plain piece of paper in half vertically to crease it, then open it and lay it flat. Glue the half-portrait to the paper aligning the middle of the face with the crease.

3. **Figure 3.** Align one edge of a piece of tracing paper along the middle of the portrait and tape it in place so that it can move like the page in a book.

4. Fold the tracing paper over the portrait and trace the outline of the face and its features. Draw carefully and accurately.

5. When you have completed the tracing, fold the tracing paper to the empty side of the paper to complete the face.

6. Compare your completed face with the one made by your partner.

Part C. Make it Symmetrical

1. Work with a partner.

2. Each of you will work with different colored clay.

3. Look back at your diagrams from Part A.

4. Choose one animal to model in clay. Mold the shape for half of the animal.

5. Your partner should model the other half of the animal.

6. Fully assemble the new animal and determine if you have re-created the whole animal.

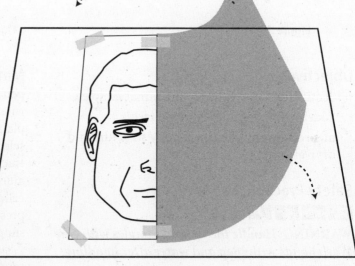

Figure 3

Classic **Lab** 26, **Is that symmetrical?** continued

Data and Observations
Table 1

Symmetry Data				
Animal	**Movement**	**Habitat**	**Symmetry**	**Diagram**

Analyze and Conclude

1. Which animals showed bilateral symmetry? Which showed radial symmetry?

_____

_____

2. How do animals with radial symmetry compare with animals with bilateral symmetry?

_____

_____

3. How could bilateral symmetry be advantageous when it comes to escaping from predators?

_____

_____

_____

4. Error Analysis What are some possible sources of error in your activity?

_____

_____

_____

5. Is your face truly symmetrical? Explain.

_____

_____

_____

6. Were you and your partner able to construct an accurate model of the animal? Looking at all the samples in the class, which type of symmetry seems easier to model?

_____

_____

_____

Inquiry Extensions

1. Choose five or six common objects around your home, such as a ladder, a plate, or a tool. Find one example of bilateral symmetry and one of radial symmetry. Write a paragraph describing how the symmetry of each object relates to or supports its function.

2. Observe as many animals as possible in your local area. Keep a list of the animals and later draw diagrams of certain ones and mark their lines of symmetry. Do most animals that you see have bilateral or radial symmetry? Why do you suppose that is?

Design Your Own
Lab 27

Which will the worm choose?

Earthworms, like other animals, have a preference when given the choice between two environmental extremes. Think about your preferences. Do you like to sleep in total darkness, or with a light on? Do you prefer hot temperatures or cold temperatures? In this lab, you will design an experiment that looks at the preferences of earthworms.

Problem
Think about places that you are most likely to see earthworms. Determine if there are certain conditions that earthworms favor over others.

Objectives
- Identify environmental factors that a worm might favor.
- Design a laboratory experiment to determine which condition an earthworm favors.
- Compare the behaviors of two earthworms under a variety of conditions.
- Draw a conclusion about the conditions preferred by these organisms.

Safety Precautions

Possible Materials
stopwatch
earthworms (2)
water
clean spray bottle or dropper
paper towels
shallow pan
cardboard
flashlight
soil
sand
non-mercury thermometer
ruler

Hypothesis
Use what you know about earthworms to write a hypothesis indicating which of a pair of related environmental conditions earthworms prefer.

_____

_____

_____

_____

Plan the Experiment

1. Read and complete the lab safety form.

2. Decide on a procedure to use to test the preference of the worms. Your teacher will review the proper handling of live animals with you. In addition, refer to **Figure 1**. It demonstrates an acceptable method for keeping earthworms moist. Do not, however, leave the worms in a deep puddle—they will drown.

3. In the space provided below, write your procedure for testing the preference of the animals. Include the materials you will use.

4. Identify the independent variable, dependent variable, control group, and constants.

5. Decide how you will determine which factor the worms prefer. Try watching their behavior over a period of time and watch which environmental factor they tend to move toward. You may want to run your trial twice—or if time allows, several times—to make sure that your observations are accurate.

6. Determine how you will record your data and observations and when you will record it. Create a data table to record your observations of the worms' movements over a period of time.

Check the Plan

1. Make sure your teacher has approved your experimental plan before you proceed.

2. Be sure that a control group is included in your experiment and that the experimental groups vary in one way only.

3. Observe the behavior of your earthworms over a pre-determined period of time.

4. When you have completed the experiment, return the earthworms to their original container and dispose of the other materials as directed by your teacher.

5. Wash your hands with soap and water.

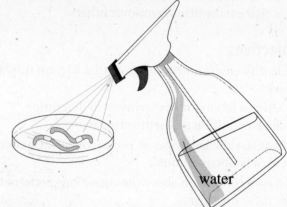

Figure 1

Record the Plan

In the space below, write your experimental procedure and make a sketch of your experimental setup.

Design Your Own **Lab** 27, **Which will the worm choose?** continued

Data and Observations

1. In the space below, make drawings of the worms at the beginning and the end of the experiment.

Analyze and Conclude

1. Which environmental factor did you choose to investigate? What was it about your knowledge of worm behavior that led you to choose to investigate this factor?

_____

_____

_____

2. Which environment did the worms prefer? Did the worms' behavior support your hypothesis?

_____

_____

_____

3. What is it about an earthworm's structure and requirements for life that explain their responses to your environmental conditions?

_____

_____

_____

4. Describe the variables that were controlled in your experiment. Why is it important that these variables remain constant?

_____

_____

_____

_____

5. **Error Analysis** What were some possible sources of error in your experiment?

_____

_____

_____

_____

6. Exchange your experimental design and results with another group. What do their data indicate about the general behavior of earthworms?

_____

_____

_____

_____

Write and Discuss

Write a short paragraph describing your findings and indicating whether or not they support your hypothesis. Did both of the worms you studied behave in the same manner? Discuss any questions your results might have raised.

_____

_____

_____

_____

Inquiry Extensions

1. What other earthworm behaviors could you investigate? Develop a hypothesis and a procedure for testing it. What would you expect to see?

2. Develop a hypothesis about the role of earthworms in the biological niche they inhabit. Write an experimental procedure to test your hypothesis. If your teacher approves of your plan, conduct the experiment and report your results.

Design Your Own
Lab 28

What is living in the leaf litter?

Have you ever walked in the woods and wondered what creatures were living in the soil beneath you? How do these organisms impact the environment, and what role do they play in the food web?

Many organisms live in the soil and leaf litter above the soil. These organisms play a role in the health of the habitat and can impact the environment in both positive and negative ways. Arthropods and other organisms in the leaf litter feed on items found there, as well as on each other. In turn, other animals feed on them. In this experiment, you will discover what types of organisms live in the soil in your area and infer the role these organisms play in the soil's food web.

Problem

A species of bird that is strictly insectivorous has changed its migration path. Determine what food is available to the birds.

Objectives

- Observe organisms found in soil or leaf litter.
- Identify the organisms.

Safety Precautions

WARNING: *Use care when handling the scissors and wire screening; their edges are sharp and might cut or puncture the skin.*

Possible Materials

2-L clear plastic bottle
scissors
trowel
cheesecloth or plastic wrap
rubber bands
desk lamp
magnifying lens
jars—one large, one small
1/4-inch mesh wire screen (10-cm square)
forceps
spoons
500–1000 mL soil sample
leaf litter
pine cones
identification guide

Hypothesis

Use what you know about arthropods to write a hypothesis about their presence in the soil environment.

_____

_____

_____

_____

Plan the Experiment

1. Read and complete the lab safety form.
2. Choose one of the following substances to test for arthropods: leaf litter, dry sandy soil, soil near a pond, or pine cones and pine needles from a forest. Which type of substance do you think will have a varied and diverse population of arthropods?
3. Decide on a procedure to collect and examine the arthropods from the soil or leaf sample. In the space provided, write your procedure for collecting and separating the arthropods. Include the materials you will use.
4. Decide how you will record your data. Create a data table to hold your observations. Include room for quantitative and qualitative data on the organisms as well as detailed sketches.

Check the Plan

1. Make sure your teacher has approved your experimental design before you begin.
2. Do not handle the animals; they might bite or sting.
3. When you have completed your experiment, dispose of the materials as directed by your teacher.

Record the Plan

In the space below, write your experimental procedure and make a sketch of your experimental setup.

Data and Observations

1. Use the space below to create a data table of your findings, including a sketch of the organisms, the number found, the size, important characteristics, and a preliminary identification of each organism.

Design Your Own **Lab** 28, **What is living in the leaf litter?** continued

2. In the space below, provide detailed sketches of several of the arthropods you found and label the body parts.

Analyze and Conclude

1. How did the conditions of your soil sample change from the beginning of the lab to the end of the lab? What caused these changes?

_____

_____

_____

2. What types of animals did you find in your sample? How did you identify these organisms?

_____

_____

_____

_____

3. What factor or factors made the animals in your sample move?

_____

_____

_____

4. What was the primary method of locomotion for the animals you found? Were there any exceptions? If there were different means of locomotion available to the animal under observation, draw conclusions about how the animal would use that means in the environment.

_____

_____

_____

_____

5. **Error Analysis** What were some possible sources of error in your lab design and observations?

_____

_____

_____

6. Exchange your procedure and data with another group in your class for peer review. What do their data indicate about the presence of arthropods in the soil samples they were using?

_____

_____

_____

Write and Discuss

Write a short paragraph describing your findings and indicating whether or not they support your hypothesis.

_____

_____

_____

_____

_____

Inquiry Extensions

1. What other organisms, besides the arthropods you examined, could be present in your soil? What relationship might exist between the arthropods and these organisms?

2. How do arthropods survive the winter? What do they do if or when the soil freezes? Develop a hypothesis that would explain the effects of the seasons on these organisms and design an experiment to test it.

Classic
Lab 29

How can you analyze echinoderm relationships?

A cladogram is a diagram which shows the evolutionary relationships between different groups of organisms. By showing these relationships, cladograms essentially reconstruct the evolutionary history (or phylogeny) of these organisms. Cladograms are also sometimes known as phylogenies or phylogenic trees.

Cladograms are constructed by grouping organisms together based on their shared characteristics. Scientists collect data on the features of all the organisms they want to classify. This includes physical features, such as whether or not the animal is a vertebrate or has limbs, as well as physiological features, such as how it obtains nourishment. Scientists then analyze this data to determine which characteristics were present in common ancestors and which could have developed at a later time.

If you were to study a group of organisms, you would most likely find characteristics that all members of the group share. These are known as primitive, or original, characteristics. Characteristics shared by only a portion of the group are considered derived characteristics. Scientists believe that these are more advanced features, or adaptations, that helped the organisms survive. These derived characteristics are the basis of constructing cladograms.

In this lab, you will design your own cladograms based on the characteristics of several animal specimens. Some representative echinoderm species are shown in **Figure 1**.

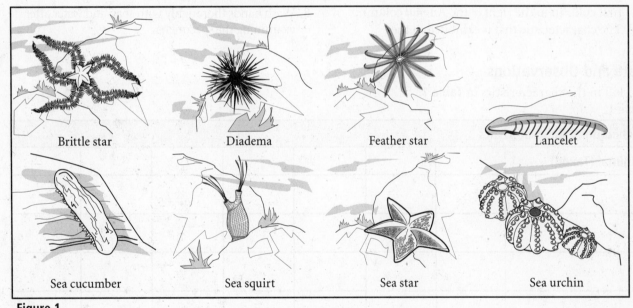

Brittle star   Diadema   Feather star   Lancelet

Sea cucumber   Sea squirt   Sea star   Sea urchin

Figure 1

Objectives

- Examine samples of echinoderms and invertebrate chordates to determine characteristics.
- Create a cladogram to represent the evolutionary relationships among these animals.
- Make inferences about the significance of these relationships.

Materials

diagrams
ruler
glue
paper
markers/colored pencils
specimens: sea star, brittle star, sea urchin, sea cucumber, feather star, sea squirt, and lancelets

Laboratory Manual

Safety Precautions

WARNING: *Sea urchin spines are very sharp and can puncture the skin.*

Procedure

1. Read and complete the lab safety form.
2. Obtain a set of echinoderms and invertebrate chordates. Lay them out on the lab table. If you are observing living specimens, handle them gently. Do not harm the animals in any way.
3. List all the characteristics you see for each animal, and assign each one to a column in the top row of **Table 1**.
4. The taxon (a group of animals or plants that share most of their characteristics) with the least number of derived characteristics should be listed in the first row. The taxon with the greatest number of derived characteristics should be listed in the last row. The characteristic that is evident in the greatest number of taxa should be listed in the first column to the right of the *Animal* column. The characteristic that is exhibited in the least number of taxa should be listed in the last column. Use plus and minus symbols to represent presence (+) or absence (−) of specific characteristics in species.
5. Determine which characteristic all the organisms have in common.
6. Look at the data, and determine the derived characteristics. The largest group of these derived characteristics will be the first to branch from the main trunk of the cladogram. Name the derived characteristic, and list all the animals that have that characteristic.
7. Look for other characteristics that are common to only a portion of the group, and add these to the cladogram until the groups can be sorted no further.
8. Wash hands thoroughly with soap and water after examining the specimens.

Data and Observations

1. Fill in the characteristics in **Table 1**.

Table 1

Echinoderm Characteristics						
Animal (Taxon)						

Classic **Lab 29, How can you analyze echinoderm relationships?** continued

2. In the space below, create your cladogram of echinoderms and invertebrate chordates.

Analyze and Conclude

1. What was the primitive characteristic for the animals you examined? Why was this characteristic of little use when designing your cladogram?

_____

_____

_____

2. What characteristics did you choose to examine? Why did you choose these?

_____

_____

_____

3. What did the characteristics you chose tell you about the way that the animal moves or eats?

_____

_____

_____

4. What is the main difference between echinoderms and invertebrate chordates?

_____

_____

_____

_____

5. **Error Analysis** What were some possible sources of error in your analysis?

_____

_____

_____

6. Which organism is most closely related to sea stars? Which is most distantly related? Explain your answer.

_____

_____

_____

_____

_____

Inquiry Extensions

1. An estimated 6000 species of echinoderms and about 1200 known species of invertebrate chordates exist. What is the evolutionary history of these species? Find examples of each group that existed long ago, and show how these animals have changed throughout their evolutionary history. Create a diagram that shows this transition, and include the time periods of each.

2. How do echinoderms and invertebrate chordates move and eat? Use a variety of materials to create a model of one organism that shows an animal's mobility and consumption methods. Share your models with the class.

Classic
Lab 30

How have frogs adapted to land and aquatic habitats?

Amphibians are the evolutionary bridge between fishes and reptiles. Frogs exemplify most of the traits that characterize amphibians. In this lab, you will observe an adult frog and identify those traits that make it suited to a terrestrial environment.

Objectives

- Observe a live frog.
- Compare and contrast a frog to humans.
- Identify useful adaptations of frogs.
- Research one adaptation.
- Make a model of the adaptation to share with the class.

Materials

live frog
paper towels
tabletop
water
pencil with an eraser
large aquarium

Safety Precautions

Procedure
Part A. Observing the Frog

1. Read and complete the lab safety form.
2. Moisten the top of the table where the frog will be placed. Sit quietly by the table, and allow time for the frog to become accustomed to its surroundings. By avoiding sudden movements, you will increase your opportunities for making accurate observations.
3. Compare the general structure of the frog's body with that of your own. Think of your body as consisting of a head, neck, trunk, and four appendages. Record your observations in **Table 1**.
4. Locate the frog's eyes. The ears are located behind and below the eyes. The eardrum is stretched across the ear opening.
5. In the human body, each of the upper append-ages consists of a series of parts called the upper arm, the forearm, the wrist, the hand, and the fingers; each of the lower appendages consists of the thigh, shank, ankle, foot and toes. Identify similar structures, if possible, in the frog. Record your observations in **Table 1**.
6. Using the eraser end of a pencil, gently prod the frog until it jumps.
7. You must observe carefully to see the frog breathe. First locate the nostrils. (Ducts lead from the nostrils to the posterior part of the mouth cavity.) Then, without touching the frog, watch the floor of the mouth (upper throat). When it is lowered, the mouth cavity enlarges.
8. Place the frog in the water at one end of the large aquarium. Observe the motion used to swim.
9. Return the live frog to the container designated by your teacher.
10. Make a diagram of a frog, and label the parts that you saw in your observations. Identify your frog as male or female.

Part B. Amphibian Adaptation

1. Look back at the observations you made of the live frog. As you have seen, amphibians show many adaptations that allow them to spend part of their life cycle in an aquatic environment and part of their life cycle in a terrestrial environment.

2. Choose one of these adaptations to study. Use resources to explore more about this particular adaptation and how it supports the amphibian in a terrestrial environment.

3. Design an interactive display or demonstration that will show your classmates why this particular adaptation is useful. Tie your demonstration to evolutionary pressures, and describe how this adaptation has provided an evolutionary advantage for the frog.

4. As part of a science symposium, present your demonstration or display to the class.

Data and Observations

Table 1

Observation Data		
Trait	**Frog**	**Human**
Body shape/length		
Neck		
Eyes		
Ears		
Nostrils		
Skin		
Feet		
Length of hip to knee and knee to foot		
Movement type/length of stride		
Breathing		

Classic **Lab** 30, **How have frogs adapted to land and aquatic habitats?** continued

Analyze and Conclude

1. How is the physical structure of a frog similar to that of a human? How is it different? What type of symmetry does a frog's body have?

_____

_____

_____

_____

2. How does a frog breathe?

_____

_____

_____

_____

3. Describe a frog's eyes. How are they different from yours? How are they the same?

_____

_____

_____

4. What adaptations make a frog suited to its life in the water and on land? Explain.

_____

_____

_____

_____

5. Which adaptation did you choose to further explore? Why did you choose this one?

_____

_____

_____

_____

_____

_____

_____

6. What conclusions did you draw from your research? Do all amphibians show the same adaptation?

_____

_____

_____

_____

7. Error Analysis What errors could have been made while observing the live frog?

_____

_____

_____

_____

Inquiry Extensions

1. Choose another amphibian, such as a salamander or newt, to observe. Compare the structures and behaviors you notice with those of the frog.

2. Many amphibians have some means of protection. Some are camouflaged, while some have a poison in their skin. Research one such adaptation, and create a short information pamphlet about it to share with your class.

Copyright © Glencoe/McGraw-Hill, a division of The McGraw-Hill Companies, Inc.

Classic

Lab 31

What are the structures and functions of a chicken egg?

Fossil evidence suggests that birds evolved from archosaurs—the line from which crocodiles and dinosaurs evolved. This indicates that dinosaurs, crocodiles, and birds are more closely related to each other than they are to turtles and lizards.

A chicken egg is made up of an egg yolk, albumen, egg membranes, and a shell. Eggshells are semipermeable. They allow gas to move in and out of the egg but keep out most liquids. Materials move in and out of the egg by osmosis—the movement of water molecules from an area of high concentration to an area of low concentration.

In this lab, you will examine chicken eggs to explore how their structures have adapted to an existence on land.

Objectives

- Identify the different parts of a chicken egg.
- Recognize how substances can pass across a membrane during osmosis.
- Infer how the egg is suited to existing on land, as opposed to in the water.

Materials

petri dish
tweezers
magnifying lens
metric ruler
2 unfertilized raw chicken eggs (the larger the better)
hard-boiled chicken egg (the larger the better)
paper towels
small plastic knife
microscope
microscope slide
cover slip
distilled water
clear corn syrup
vinegar
clear plastic cup
balance
rubber gloves
aluminum foil

Safety Precautions

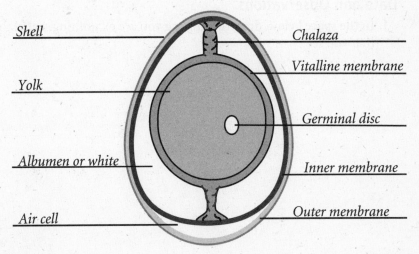

Shell
Yolk
Albumen or white
Air cell

Chalaza
Vitalline membrane
Germinal disc
Inner membrane
Outer membrane

Figure 1

Procedure

Part A. Structures of an Egg

1. Read and complete the lab safety form.

2. Put on a pair of rubber gloves, and obtain a raw egg from your teacher.

3. Carefully crack and open the egg, and place it in the petri dish. If possible, try to break the egg in half and keep as much of the yolk and white in one half of the shell. Try not to break the shell into many pieces.

4. Obtain a hard-boiled egg from your teacher. Carefully remove the shell, and cut through the hard-boiled egg with the plastic knife. Lay both halves of the egg and the broken shell on the paper towel.

5. Compare the two eggs to **Figure 1**. In the space in the *Data and Observations* section, draw and label the different parts of each egg.

6. The germinal disk is a white dot in the center of a raw egg yolk. Use a ruler to measure the diameter of that dot.

7. Compare the yolks, the albumen, and the shells of the hard-boiled egg and the raw egg using the microscope. Record your observations in **Table 1**.

Part B. Osmosis

1. Choose a raw egg, and gently wipe it clean with a paper towel. Place it on the balance, and measure the mass in grams. Record this information in **Table 2**.

2. Place the egg in a clear plastic cup, and cover it with 150 mL of vinegar.

3. Cover the cup with aluminum foil, and leave it undisturbed for two days.

4. After two days, the eggshell should have dissolved away. Wearing gloves, gently remove the egg from the beaker. Rinse it under running water, then gently dry it with a paper towel.

5. Measure the mass of the egg again, and record the mass in the data table. Also record any changes that might have occurred to the egg.

6. Measure the amount of vinegar left in the beaker, and record this information.

7. Clean and dry the cup, and place the egg back in it. Add 150 mL of clear corn syrup to the cup.

8. Cover the cup and leave undisturbed for 24 h.

9. Again wearing gloves, carefully remove the egg, and rinse it under running water.

10. Measure the mass of the egg, and record the mass and any other changes in the data table.

11. Measure the amount of corn syrup left in the beaker, and record this information in the data table.

12. Clean and dry the cup, and place the egg back in it. Add 150 mL of distilled water.

13. Repeat steps 8–11 for the egg and the distilled water.

14. Dispose of the egg as directed by your teacher.

Data and Observations

1. In the space below, draw the raw egg you are examining. Label the different parts that you see.

Classic **Lab** 31, **What are the structures and functions of a chicken egg?** continued

2. In the space below, draw a diagram of the hard-boiled egg you are examining. Label the visible parts.

Table 1

Comparison of Egg Structures					
	Shell	**Yolk**	**Albumen**	**Membranes**	**Chalazae**
Hard-boiled egg					
Raw egg					

Table 2

Osmosis in Shelled Egg						
Liquid	**Amount of Liquid**		**Mass of Egg**		**Egg Observations**	
	Before	**After**	**Before**	**After**	**Before**	**After**
Vinegar						
Corn syrup						
Distilled water						

Analyze and Conclude

1. Is the eggshell porous? Is it permeable to air? To water? How is the eggshell of a hard-boiled egg different from the shell of a raw egg?

_____

_____

_____

2. Which part of the egg is analogous to the placenta in a mammal?

_____

_____

3. How did the egg change when it was put in vinegar? Why did this occur?

_____

_____

4. How did the egg change when it was put in corn syrup? Why did this occur?

_____

_____

5. Describe the changes in the egg when it was placed in distilled water. Explain what you saw.

_____

_____

_____

6. Error Analysis What were some possible sources of error in your experiment?

_____

_____

_____

7. How is a chicken egg suited for life on land? How do you think an amphibian egg might be different, considering amphibian eggs are laid in water?

_____

_____

_____

Inquiry Extensions

1. All birds are oviparous—the young grow in eggs outside the mother's body. Some animal groups, such as fishes and reptiles, include genera that are oviparous and some that are ovoviviparous. Research what this term means. Cite some animals that fall into this category. What advantage might this give to the organisms that use it?

2. Many dinosaurs laid eggs. Research the egg-laying behavior of at least two species of dinosaur, and compare the dinosaur behavior to that of birds and reptiles. Present your findings to the class.

Design Your Own
Lab 32

What is the best way to keep warm?

Many mammals and other warm-blooded animals have some sort of insulation on their body to help them maintain a constant body temperature despite variations in the temperature surrounding them. For example, a whale has a thick layer of blubber, and a sheep has a thick wool coat. In this lab, you will model the insulating properties of wool.

Problem
Many people wear wool clothes in the winter to keep warm. How well does wool insulate when it gets wet?

Objectives
- Form a hypothesis comparing the insulating properties of wet wool socks and dry wool socks.
- Design an experiment to test the hypothesis.
- Compare the temperature of water in the socks over time.

Safety Precautions

Possible Materials
wool socks (1 pair)
1-L glass beaker
plastic containers with lids (3)
thermometers (non-mercury) (3)
hot tap water
room-temperature water
stopwatch
scissors
craft knife
rubber bands
graph paper
colored pencils

Hypothesis
Use what you know about wool as an insulating material to write a hypothesis indicating the differences between the insulating ability of dry wool socks and wet wool socks.

_____

_____

_____

_____

Plan the Experiment

1. Read and complete the lab safety form.
2. Determine how you will test the insulating properties of a wet wool sock and a dry wool sock. Assemble your experiment.
3. Identify the independent variable, dependent variable, constants, and control for your experiment.
4. Decide how you will record your data and when you will record it. Design and construct a data table to hold your experimental data on temperature, container type, and time.
5. Decide how you will present your findings to the rest of the class.

Check the Plan

1. Make sure your teacher has approved your experimental plan before you proceed.
2. Be sure that a control is included in your experiment and that the experimental groups vary in only one way.
3. **Figure 1** Use caution preparing the container lids and when pouring hot water into the containers.
4. Observe the changes in temperature in containers in wet and dry socks.
5. When you have completed the experiment, clean up your materials as directed by your teacher. Remember to wash hands with soap and water after completing the lab.

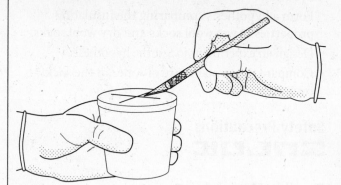

Figure 1

Record the Plan

In the space below, write your experimental procedure and make a sketch of your experimental setup.

Design Your Own **Lab** 32, **What is the best way to keep warm?** continued

Data and Observations

1. Use the space below to create a data table of your findings, including the container, temperature, and time lapsed.

2. In the space below, or on a separate sheet of graph paper, graph the results of your experiment.

Analyze and Conclude

1. How did the temperatures change in your containers?

_____

_____

2. Describe the control in your experiment. What did the control show?

_____

_____

3. What comparisons can be made between the wool socks in your experiment and the insulation that some mammals have? Use specific examples in your answer.

_____

_____

_____

4. **Error Analysis** What were some possible sources of error in your experiment?

_____

_____

5. Some manufacturers claim that their wool socks will keep you warm, even when wet. Do your findings support this claim? Explain.

_____

_____

6. Exchange your procedure and data with another group for peer review. What do their data indicate about the insulating power of wool?

_____

_____

_____

Write and Discuss

On a separate sheet of paper, write a short paragraph describing your findings and indicating whether or not they support your hypothesis. Was there a difference between the insulating ability of wet wool and dry wool? Discuss any questions your results might have raised.

Inquiry Extensions

1. How would you design an experiment to compare the insulating properties of wool with those of another fabric, such as cotton or rayon, or other insulating materials? What would you do differently?

2. Research the insulation of animals that live in water and animals that live on land. What types of tissues keep them warm?

Classic
Lab 33

How do we learn?

You have been a student for long enough to know that some things are easier to learn than others. What happens when we are presented with a new task? What helps people remember new tasks? What interferes with performance?

In this lab, you will design a test that examines the way a subject masters a new task.

Objectives

- Conduct an experiment to answer questions about human learning.
- Make predictions about learning and performance.
- Communicate your findings in an appropriate manner.

Materials

pencil or marker
maze puzzle (12 copies)
portable CD or MP3 player with earphones
music or voice recording
stopwatch

Procedure

1. Read and complete the lab safety form.

2. Work with a partner. Before you begin the experiment, read through the procedure and make a prediction about the effects of the conditions.

3. **Figure 1** Set up a maze race exercise, as shown below. Designate one person as the racer and the other as the timer.

4. Have the racer complete the maze while looking only at the reflection of his or her hands in the mirror.

Figure 1

5. Use the stopwatch to time the racer's performance, and record the data in **Table 1.** Repeat this exercise twice more with fresh copies of the maze. This will complete trials 1–3.

6. For trials 4–6, repeat the exercise with a new copy of the same maze, but this time have the racer listen to music or a voice recording while performing the task.

7. Record the time for the second set of trials in **Table 1.**

8. For trials 7–12, repeat steps 4–7, but do not use the mirror. Have the racer look directly at the paper. Record the results in **Table 2.**

Data and Observations

Table 1

Trial	Results With Mirror
1	
2	
3	
4	
5	
6	

Table 2

Trial	Results Without Mirror
7	
8	
9	
10	
11	
12	

Laboratory Manual

Classic **Lab 33, How do we learn?** continued

Analyze and Conclude

1. Did the racer's performance support your prediction? Explain.

_____

_____

_____

2. By the end of trial 12, was there overall improvement in completing the task? Explain.

_____

_____

_____

3. Based on your observations and data, how did the racer perform when completing the task with the stressor (the distraction)? Explain.

_____

_____

_____

4. Think of an animal learning a new behavior. What advantage might there be for an animal that can learn under stress?

_____

_____

_____

5. Error Analysis What were some possible sources of error in your experiment?

_____

_____

_____

6. Share your data with other students. Discuss how the data of other groups compares with yours.

_____

_____

_____

7. Use the space below to make a line graph showing the results of your experiment. Using a different color, draw an additional line to show your prediction of the results if trials 7–9 were repeated two or three more times immediately following trial 12. What would you expect to see?

Inquiry Extensions

1. How does time impact memory? Create an experiment that investigates how long people remember what they learn.

2. Have you ever noticed that you can remember all the words to your favorite songs but cannot remember the formulas for respiration or photosynthesis? Take a difficult concept you have learned in biology, and write it as lyrics to a familiar tune that makes it easy to remember. Present your song to the class.

Classic
Lab 34

How long can you last?

Your body has three types of muscles: smooth, cardiac, and skeletal. Muscle cells can only contract or relax, so skeletal muscle groups must work in pairs. When one muscle group contracts, the opposing muscle group relaxes to its original shape. For example, when you bend your elbow, the biceps group on your upper arm contracts. As the biceps on the front of your arm contract, the triceps on the back of your arm relax to their original length. When you want to straighten your elbow, the process works in reverse. The triceps contract while the biceps relax.

In this lab, you will be examining the way that muscles work together in your body to squeeze a rubber bulb. You will be working to see what impact fatigue and repetitive work has on the muscles in your hand, arm, and leg.

Objectives

- Assemble a muscle-testing device based on directions and diagrams.
- Test the muscle fatigue experienced after repetitive motion over a period of one minute.
- Serve as a counter and recorder as other group members test muscle fatigue.
- Draw conclusions about muscle fatigue.

Materials

rubber bulb
1/2-inch plastic or vinyl hose, 1 m in length
1/2-inch PVC pipe, 20 cm in length
ring stand
paper flag, 2.5 cm square; red on one side, white on the other
stopwatch
cellophane tape
duct tape
first aid tape

Safety Precautions

WARNING: *Do not pull on the tubing—the apparatus might become unstable and fall over.*

Procedure

Part A. Assembling the Device

1. Read and complete the lab safety form.

2. In your group, assemble the muscle fatigue device as indicated in **Figures 1** and **2**. Attach a small rubber bulb to the end of a hose. (If necessary, cut a half-inch slit in the hose to allow enough room for the nozzle of the bulb.) The hose should then be inserted into the small length of PVC pipe and the entire device held up by a ring stand as shown in **Figure 1**. Use duct tape to secure both connections.

3. Tape a small paper flag over the top of the pipe so that it can move freely but will still reset itself. Tape it so that the white side is facing up.

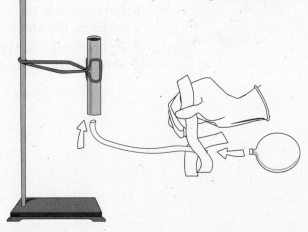

Figure 1

4. Test your device by squeezing the bulb, as shown in **Figure 2**. The air should lift the flag, making the red side visible, as shown in **Figure 3**. When the bulb is released, the flag should return to its starting position.

5. Decide which group member will act as Observer 1, Observer 2, and Tester. You will be rotating positions as time allows.

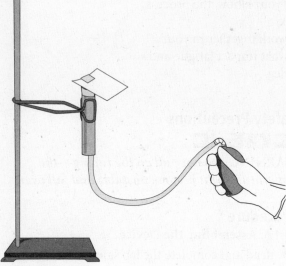

Figure 2

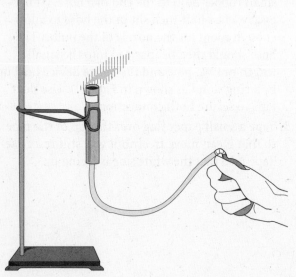

Figure 3

Part B. Testing for Fatigue

1. Complete the data table on the next page to hold the observations and data gathered in this experiment. The data table should have room for the names of each group member acting as the Tester, muscle group tested, the number of compressions in one minute, the number of time the flag lifts in one minute, and any comments the tester had after each test.

2. Start with the first Tester. This person will place the bulb in his or her hand. When Observer 1 gives the go-ahead, the Tester squeezes the bulb as many times as he or she can in the span of one minute.

3. Observer 1 has the job of timing one minute and also of counting the number of times the Tester squeezes the bulb. This information should be put in **Table 1**.

4. Observer 2 should position his or her eyes at the same level as the top of the tube, then count the number of times the red side of the flag appears during the one-minute trial. This information should be recorded in **Table 1**. The Tester should also insert any comments he or she has about muscle fatigue in **Table 1** at this point. After allowing a 15-s rest, repeat steps 2-4 for a second trial.

5. Keeping the same roles, the Tester will now place the bulb between the forearm and the upper arm (on the inside of the elbow). This will test his or her arm muscles.

6. Conduct the test for one minute, with Observer 1 and Observer 2 watching and counting the number of squeezes and the number of times the red flag appears. Repeat this test for a second trial.

7. The same Tester should then place the bulb behind the knee to test his or her leg muscles. Conduct two trials.

8. Rotate roles so that each member of the group performs all three tests.

9. Follow the instructions given by your teacher about disassembling your device.

Classic **Lab** 34, **How long can you last?** continued

Data and Observations
Table 1

Fatigue Data						
		Trial 1		Trial 2		Comments
		Number of Squeezes	Number of Red Flags	Number of Squeezes	Number of Red Flags	
Tester 1	Hand					
	Arm					
	Leg					
Tester 2	Hand					
	Arm					
	Leg					
Tester 3	Hand					
	Arm					
	Leg					

Analyze and Conclude

1. Describe the motion of the arm muscles, leg muscles, and hand muscles as the bulb was squeezed.

_____

_____

_____

_____

2. What is muscle fatigue? Describe the muscle fatigue you found in this exercise.

_____

_____

_____

_____

3. Which movement was easiest for you? Which was most difficult? Why do you think that may have been?

_____

_____

_____

4. Which muscle group became fatigued the quickest? Which was least fatigued after the one-minute trial?

_____

_____

_____

5. **Error Analysis** What were some possible sources of error in your experiment?

_____

_____

_____

_____

6. How did your results compare with those of your teammates? Can you think of reasons why there might be differences?

_____

_____

_____

_____

Inquiry Extensions

1. How does resting the muscles between trials impact the results? Conduct the experiment again but allow each Tester the opportunity to rest for 30 s before resuming with the same muscle group. What differences, if any, are there in the results? Explain the differences.

2. Is there another way to test the endurance of these muscle groups? Conduct an experiment in which you time isometric muscle contractions (for example, by standing on one leg, or by using your arm to hold your body at an angle against a wall or table) for one minute, then repeat the trial after a 30-s rest. At what point(s) were the muscles fatigued and unable to continue their work? Do the Testers report that this test was easier or harder than the bulb test? What conclusions can you draw about continuous muscle contractions as opposed to repetitive contractions?

Design Your Own
Lab 35

How quickly do you respond?

Your nervous system receives information about what is happening both inside and outside your body. Any change or signal in the environment that can make an organism react is called a stimulus. Your nervous system will analyze the stimulus and initiate a response or a reaction. It helps you move, think, feel pain, and enjoy a chocolate-chip cookie. Your nervous system also plays a role in maintaining homeostasis and recognizing basic needs of survival such as oxygen, water, and nutrients.

Problem
Design a lab experiment that measures driver reaction time for you and your lab partners. *Under no circumstances should any experimental plan be carried out in a real car.*

Objectives
- Form a hypothesis about the effect that one variable, such as time of day, has on reaction time.
- Design an experiment to test the effect of your variable on hand and foot reaction times.
- Compare the results of reaction times with and without the variable.

Safety Precautions
◌ ⚒ ⚞

Possible Materials
stopwatch
cover of frying pan (for steering wheel)
small blocks of wood (for brake and gas pedals) (2)
rubber mat
rubber ball

Hypothesis
Use what you know about the nervous system and your own response time to write a hypothesis indicating how a driver's reaction time is affected by a variable you determine.

_____

_____

_____

_____

Plan the Experiment

1. Read and complete the lab safety form.
2. Choose a way to test eye-to-foot reaction time and eye-to-hand reaction time.
3. Decide on your procedure for collecting your data. In the space provided, write your procedure for testing the reaction times of your lab partners. Include the materials you will use.
4. Identify the independent variable, dependent variable, constants, and control group.
5. Decide how you will record your data and when you will record it. Design a data table to collect information.

Check the Plan

1. Make sure your teacher has approved your experimental plan before you proceed.
2. Be sure that a control is included in your experiment.

Record the Plan

In the space below, write your experimental procedure and make a sketch of your experimental setup.

Design Your Own **Lab** 35, **How quickly do you respond?** continued

Data and Observations

1. Use the space below to create a data table of your findings, including the type of reaction being tested, the reaction time of each person, and the length of time that has passed.

Analyze and Conclude

1. What relationship did you find between reaction time and the variable you selected? Explain.

   _____

   _____

   _____

2. Based on your observations, what recommendations would you make for teenage drivers? Explain.

   _____

   _____

   _____

3. Did you see any differences between the reaction time between eyes to hand and eyes to foot? Explain.

   _____

   _____

4. Describe the control in your experiment. What did the control show?

_____

_____

5. Error Analysis What were some possible sources of error in your experiment?

_____

_____

_____

6. Exchange your procedure and data with another group in your class for peer review. What do their data indicate about reaction times?

_____

_____

_____

Write and Discuss

Write a short paragraph describing your findings and indicating whether or not they support your hypothesis. Discuss any questions your results might have raised.

_____

_____

_____

_____

Inquiry Extensions

1. Cell phone use while driving is a controversial issue. Many people now use hands-free devices on their phones so they can pay more attention to the road, but some people question the safety of these devices as well. Design an experiment that compares the reaction time of someone who is using a hand-held phone and someone who is using a hands-free device. *Under no circumstances should any experiment be carried out in a real car.* Why do you think some states fine drivers for talking on cell phones? Relate this to your experimental data.

2. When does stimulus turn into stress? Generally, a stimulus can be a single, simple event such as an itch or stubbing one's toe. Stress, on the other hand, tends to describe a set of stimuli that prompt more intense, and sometimes long-lasting, physiological and emotional responses. (Negative stressors cause *distress*, while positive stressors cause *eustress*.) Devise a journal to track a few hours of a given day. Record a selection of stimuli and your responses to them, then characterize each stimulus. Were they simple stimuli or stressors? What was your recovery time? Are the stressors acute or chronic? When you have completed gathering the data, create a chart or graph to show duration and intensity of the selected events and your responses.

Design Your Own

Lab 36

How much air can your lungs hold?

Every day you breathe in and out thousands of times. How much air do you take into your lungs each time? What conditions influence your lung capacity? Imagine that a friend who is close to you in age will be coming to your area to participate in a charity walk-a-thon with you. The air temperature in your friend's hometown is dramatically different from the typical temperatures in your area at this time of year. Will this temperature difference affect your friend's lung capacity?

Problem
Lung capacity can be affected by environmental factors.

Objectives
- Identify a factor that influences lung capacity.
- Design an experiment to test that factor.
- Draw conclusions about what impacts lung capacity.

Safety Precautions

WARNING: *Do not share balloons with other classmates. Do not put balloons or broken pieces of a balloon in the mouth; this presents a choking hazard. Students who have asthma, breathing difficulties, or a latex allergy should discuss their participation with the teacher.*

Possible Materials
round balloons (12-inch maximum diameter)
thermometer (non-mercury)
measuring tape
string
metric ruler
calculator

Hypothesis
Use what you know about lung capacity to write a hypothesis that predicts the impact air temperature has on lung capacity.

_____

_____

_____

_____

Plan the Experiment

1. Read and complete the lab safety form.
2. Make a list of the factors that might influence the lung capacity of the average high school student. Be sure to mention the factors cited in your hypothesis.
3. Decide on a procedure for testing your hypothesis. In the space provided, write your procedure for testing lung capacity. Include a list of the materials you will use.
4. Identify the independent variable, dependent variable, constants, and control group.
5. Decide how you will record your data and when you will record it. Design a data table to collect information about change in lung capacity in cubic centimeters.

Check the Plan

1. Be sure that a control group is included in your experiment and that the experimental groups vary in only one way.
2. Make sure your teacher has approved your experimental plan before you proceed.
3. When you have completed your experiment, dispose of materials as directed by your teacher.

Record the Plan

In the space below, write your experimental procedure and make a sketch of your experimental setup.

Design Your Own **Lab** 36, **How much air can your lungs hold?** continued

Data and Observations

1. In the space below, create a data table to hold the information gathered in this experiment.

Analyze and Conclude

1. Why might it be important to know a person's lung capacity?

_____

_____

_____

2. What did you learn from your experiment about the factors that you studied?

_____

_____

_____

3. How does your lung capacity differ from that of other students in your class? What factors might account for these differences?

_____

_____

_____

_____

4. How might you design your experiment differently next time?

_____

_____

_____

5. **Error Analysis** What were some possible sources of error in your experiment?

_____

_____

_____

_____

6. Exchange your procedure and data with another group in your class for peer review. What do their data indicate about the impact of different factors on lung capacity?

_____

_____

_____

_____

Write and Discuss

Write a short paragraph describing your findings and indicating whether or not they support your hypothesis. Discuss any questions your results might have raised.

_____

_____

_____

_____

Inquiry Extensions

1. What differences would you expect to see in the lung capacity of smokers as compared to nonsmokers, and as compared to nonsmokers who live with smokers? Design a questionnaire for the participants in your study to determine their exposure to cigarette smoke and other factors that can affect lung capacity. Then design an experiment to test their lung capacities. Share your findings with the rest of your class.

2. What other environmental factors, such as smog or altitude, impact lung capacity? Are there certain professions or chronic diseases that cause decreased lung capacity? Design an experiment to study these factors. Keep in mind that you might not be able to conduct your experiment due to geographic location or season, but predict what changes you might see. Follow up with research to find data on the factors or populations you chose to study.

Copyright © Glencoe/McGraw-Hill, a division of The McGraw-Hill Companies, Inc.

Classic
Lab 37

How healthy are they?

When people visit the doctor for a check up they usually have a urine sample taken. A urine sample can often be useful in detecting medical conditions that might not show other symptoms. Normal, healthy urine contains little or no glucose or protein. Glucose in the urine might be an indication that the person has diabetes. Diabetes is a disease where the body cannot use enough glucose from the blood. If there is protein in the urine, this might be a sign that the kidneys are not functioning properly. In this lab, you will be testing simulated urine samples to try to diagnose diabetes or kidney diseases.

Objectives
- Test simulated urine samples for the presence of glucose using glucose test strips.
- Test simulated urine samples for the presence of protein using Biuret solution.
- Create a data table.
- Interpret test results.

Materials
test tubes (6)
test-tube rack
plastic droppers (6)
water
glucose solution
protein solution
glucose test strips (6)
large pipettes for each sample
Biuret solution
simulated urine samples (3)
wax pencil
white paper or paper towels

Safety Precautions

WARNING: *Use caution with the Biuret solution. It is corrosive. It can irritate the eyes, skin, or respiratory tract, and should NOT be ingested. If contact occurs, flush the affected area with cold water. It might also stain clothing.*

Procedure
Part A. Test for Glucose

1. Read and complete the lab safety form.
2. Create a data table that will hold the data you gather during the course of this lab. There is a sample data table included in the next section.
3. Label six test tubes in the following way: *G* for glucose, *P* for protein, *W* for water and *1, 2,* and *3* for the three simulated urine samples.
4. **Figure 1** shows you how to place the test tubes in the test-tube rack.
5. Obtain six glucose strips and label them in the same fashion: *G, P, W, 1, 2,* and *3*.

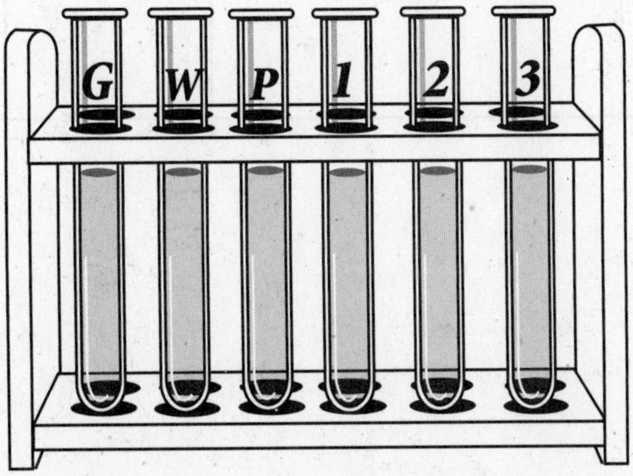

Figure 1

6. Using a large pipette, fill each test tube about ¾ full with the appropriate solution.

7. Place the *G* test strip on the clean paper towel. Use a clean dropper to pick up some of the liquid from the *G* test tube.

8. **Figure 2** shows you how to drop 2 drops of the glucose solution on the glucose test strip.

9. Record any change of color in your table. If there is no change, write "No change".

10. Repeat steps 7–9 for each of the solutions, recording your observations in your data table. Be sure to complete Part A before continuing with Part B.

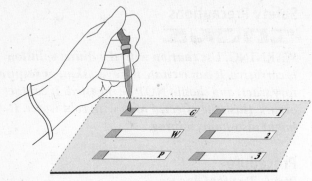

Figure 2

Part B. Test for Protein

1. Get a bottle of Biuret solution from your teacher. Use caution: Biuret solution is corrosive and can irritate the skin, eyes, and respiratory tract. If contact occurs, flush the affected area with cold water. The solution can also stain clothing.

2. Take note of the original color of the solution.

3. Carefully add 30 drops of the solution to the test tube labeled *G*.

4. Gently swirl the test tube to mix the liquids.

5. Note any color change. You might want to hold the tube in front of a white paper towel to provide a neutral background.

6. Observe any changes and record the changes in **Table 1**.

7. Repeat steps 3–5 for the remaining solutions.

8. Clean the equipment and dispose of the liquids as directed by your teacher. Wash your hands with soap and water.

Data and Observations
Table 1

Simulated Urine Sample Data						
Test For	Water	Glucose	Protein	Patient 1	Patient 2	Patient 3
Glucose						
Protein						

Classic **Lab 37, How healthy are they?** continued

Analyze and Conclude

1. What do the changes you saw in Part A of the laboratory tell you about the patients and the original solutions? Explain.

   _____

   _____

   _____

   _____

   _____

2. What do the changes you saw in Part B tell you about the patients and the original solutions?

   _____

   _____

   _____

   _____

   _____

3. Which of the three patients showed a normal urine sample? How do you know?

   _____

   _____

   _____

   _____

4. Should one of the patients be tested further for diabetes? Which one? How do you know?

   _____

   _____

   _____

   _____

   _____

5. Are any of the patients showing signs of kidney disease? Explain.

_____

_____

_____

6. Error Analysis What are possible sources of error in your experiment?

_____

_____

_____

_____

_____

7. Is the data gathered here enough for a doctor to make a diagnosis? Should the doctor explore further with more tests? Explain your answer.

_____

_____

_____

_____

_____

Inquiry Extensions

1. Do diet and timing have an impact on these test results? Conduct research online or in the library to see how test results are affected when food has been ingested shortly before the tests. Present your findings to the class in the form of a public service brochure.

2. What other tests can be done on urine? Find an example of another common test involving urine and write the procedure for an experiment to test urine for that condition.

Design Your Own

Lab 38

How do you digest protein?

You probably eat protein every day. Protein is found in such foods as eggs, meat, poultry, fish, dairy products, nuts, beans, and lentils. The body uses protein for tissue growth and repair. Proteins are digested in the stomach by digestive chemicals and a mechanical process that occurs as the stomach churns. Pepsin is the enzyme found in digestive juices that chemically digests the proteins in foods by breaking them into shorter chains of amino acids. Pepsin is most effective in the acidic environment of the stomach.

Problem

Design an experiment that determines what conditions are needed for the digestion of proteins in the stomach.

Objectives

- Design an experiment.
- Compare conditions for the function of pepsin in the digestive process.
- Collect and interpret data, and draw conclusions about the conditions within the stomach.

Safety Precautions

WARNING: *Excercise caution when handling hydrochloric acid.*

Possible Materials

test-tube rack
2% pepsin solution
blue litmus paper
boiled egg white or firm tofu
plastic knife
ruler
graduated cylinder
test tubes with stoppers

marking pencil
2% hydrochloric acid solution
stirring rod (glass)

Hypothesis

Use what you know about digestion and proteins to write a hypothesis that explains the conditions that could accelerate digestion in the stomach and why this would occur.

_____

_____

_____

_____

Plan the Experiment

1. Read and complete the lab safety form.
2. Decide on a source of protein to test.
3. Decide on a procedure for testing the effects of acidic conditions on the digestion of protein. Your experiment might take two days to complete.
4. Identify the independent variable, dependent variable, constants, and control group.
5. Decide how you will record your data. Design a data table to record the information that you collect.

Check the Plan

1. Be sure that a control group is included in your experiment and that the experimental groups only vary in one way.
2. Make sure your teacher has approved your experimental plan before you proceed.
3. When you have completed the experiment, dispose of the liquid as directed by your teacher.

Record the Plan

In the space below, write your experimental procedure and make a sketch of your experimental setup.

Data and Observations

1. Use the space below to create a data table of your findings, including the appearance of the protein source over two days.

Analyze and Conclude

1. Which chemicals were best at digesting the protein you examined? How do you know?

_____

_____

_____

2. Does the chemical digestion of protein happen quickly or slowly? Explain.

_____

_____

_____

3. Did you cut the pieces of protein into blocks the same size? Why would that be important?

_____

_____

_____

4. What did your experiment show about the ability of pepsin to digest protein?

_____

_____

_____

5. Error Analysis What were some possible sources of error in your experiment?

_____

_____

_____

6. Describe the control in your experiment. What did the control show?

_____

_____

_____

7. Exchange your procedure and data with another group in the class for peer review. What do their data indicate about the conditions affecting protein digestion?

_____

_____

_____

Write and Discuss

Write a short paragraph describing your findings and indicating whether or not they support your hypothesis. Discuss any questions your results might have raised.

_____

_____

_____

_____

Inquiry Extensions

1. Does digestion occur faster if the particles of protein are smaller? Design a test which examines how the size of particles impacts digestion rate.

2. What other factors could impact the rate of digestion? Would the presence of other food in the stomach play a role? Would more liquid accelerate the process? Choose one additional variable to test, and design an experiment to test it.

Laboratory Manual

Classic
Lab 39

How does a body grow?

As the human body grows and develops, it increases in size. The proportions of some parts of the body also change in relation to each other. Males and females develop at different times and at different rates. As you complete this lab, you will discover some proportional relationships of body parts evident in different ages.

Objectives
- Compare the average height of humans with the average length of body parts during various stages of human development.
- Graph the average height of humans.
- Analyze rates of human development, male or female, based on the data assembled and graphed.

Materials
metric ruler
graph paper
calculator
colored pencils

Procedure
Part A. Growth and Development in Humans
1. Read and complete the lab safety form.
2. **Figure 1** shows four stages of development in the life of a human. Note how some parts of the body are larger in proportion to the entire body at various stages of development.
3. **Table 1** shows the average height of a male and female at each of these four stages of human development. Keep in mind that these are the median heights—about half of all people are taller, and about half are shorter.

Figure 1

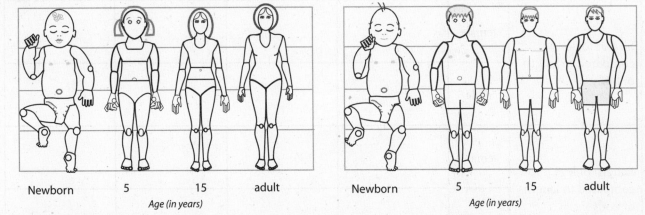

Newborn   5   15   adult   Newborn   5   15   adult

Age (in years)   *Age (in years)*

Differential growth rates in humans. Chart shows head, torso and leg in relation to puberty from birth to adulthood.

Table 1

Average Height at Selected Ages				
	Newborn	**Five Years**	**Fifteen Years**	**Adult**
Average height : male (in cm)	50	109	170	177
Average height: female (in cm)	47	107	162	163

Part B. Graphing Proportions of Body Parts to Total Height

1. Gather information about how the lengths of certain body parts in each of the four stages of development compare to the total length of each body in **Figure 1**. Use your ruler to measure the total length of each figure and the length of the head and torso. (The torso is the part of the body from the shoulders to the pelvis.)

2. Use your calculator to convert your measurements into percentages. Complete **Table 2** with the information you have obtained.

3. Use the graph paper to make a line graph of the data in **Table 2**. Let the *x*-axis be percentage of total body length, and the *y*-axis be age. Use different colored pencils for the head, torso, and leg measurements at each age.

Data and Observations

Table 2

Data for Graphing Proportions of Body Parts to Total Height						
		Newborn	**Five Years**	**Fifteen Years**	**Adult**
Size of head compared to length of body	female				
	male				
Size of torso compared to length of body	female				
	male				
Length of legs compared to length of body	female				
	male				

Laboratory Manual

Classic **Lab 39, How does a body grow?** continued

Analyze and Conclude

1. How do the proportions for head size, torso size, and leg length change from infancy to adulthood?

_____

_____

_____

2. What can you conclude about the rate at which different parts of your body grow? Explain.

_____

_____

_____

3. Was it useful to represent the data from this lab in the form of a table and in a line graph? Explain.

_____

_____

_____

4. Based on your findings, how would you conclude that other measurements of body parts to total body length, for instance, head circumference or arm length, might change as a person grows?

_____

_____

_____

_____

5. Based on your findings, if you were given the head, torso, and leg proportions of an unseen individual whose growth pattern was within normal parameters, do you think you could tell if that person was an infant, a child, a teen, or an adult? Explain.

_____

_____

_____

_____

6. Based on your findings, if you were given the age, head, torso, and leg proportions of an unseen individual whose growth pattern was within normal parameters, do you think you could make a reasonable estimate of that person's height? Explain.

_____

_____

_____

7. Error Analysis What are possible sources of error in this exercise?

_____

_____

_____

Inquiry Extensions

1. How much do ratios differ if people are taller or shorter than the median heights shown in **Table 1**? Develop a plan to obtain additional images that you can measure and compare ratios as in **Table 2**.

2. Based on your age, can you predict what your own body ratios will be? Use the calculations here to make an estimate of the ratio of your head size, torso size, and leg length. Then, ask another classmate to measure your height and the corresponding measurements. Determine if your estimates were correct. Report your findings to the class.

Classic
Lab 40

Who needs a banana peel?

Bacteria are present everywhere. Many bacteria can cause disease and decay, but in most cases, you remain disease-free because your skin serves as a barrier between the bacteria and the more delicate tissues inside. The peel on a banana is similar to the skin on your body. In this lab, you will test the effectiveness of a banana peel in preventing the decay of the fruit.

Objectives

- Prepare and observe bananas over a period of five days.
- Model the skin's defense against disease using banana peels.
- Conduct an experiment controlling variables.
- Form a conclusion about the necessity of washing and cleaning cuts to prevent disease.

Materials

sealable plastic bags (4)
fresh bananas (4)
rotten banana
permanent marker
water
paper towel
toothpick
cotton swab
rubbing alcohol

Safety Precautions

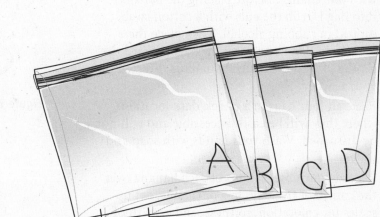

Procedure

1. Read and complete the lab safety form.
2. Label the four plastic bags with your name and the letters *A*, *B*, *C*, and *D*.
3. Wash the fresh bananas, and then dry them with a paper towel.

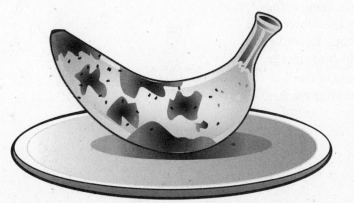

4. **Figure 1** Place one banana in Bag A. Seal the bag, and set it aside.

5. **Figure 2** Gently insert a toothpick through the peel of the rotten banana and into the fruit. Then, using the same toothpick, lightly run the tip of the toothpick down the side of the second fresh banana. Do not pierce the peel of the second banana, as shown in **Figure 3**. Use caution when handling the toothpick; it could pierce your skin. Repeat three times, on different parts of the banana. Place the second banana in Bag B, and seal the bag. Discard the toothpick.

6. Take a new toothpick. Insert it into the rotten banana. Then, using the same toothpick, make a shallow, 2.5-cm cut in the peel of the third fresh banana, being careful not to insert the toothpick into the fruit itself. Repeat this three more times, piercing the skin of the banana each time. Place the banana into Bag C, and seal the bag. Discard the toothpick.

7. Use the last fresh banana, and repeat step 6 with one change. Before placing the banana into Bag D, rub the cuts with a cotton swab dipped in rubbing alcohol. Then place the banana in Bag D, and seal the bag. Discard the toothpick and the rotten banana as directed by your teacher.

8. Place all four bags in a warm, dark location where they will be easily accessible and will not be disturbed. Wash your hands with soap and water.

9. Record your observations of each banana over the course of five days in a data table. Set up scales for coloration, softness, and growth of fungi. Use **Table 1** provided on the next page.

10. Every day, for a total of five days, remove the bananas in their bags from storage. Observe the bananas without opening the bags. Record your observations, then return the bags to storage.

11. At the end of the activity, dispose of the unopened bags as instructed by your teacher.

Figure 1

Figure 2

Figure 3

Classic **Lab 40, Who needs a banana peel?** continued

Data and Observations

Table 1

Banana Observation Data				
Day	Banana 1 (no contact with rotting fruit)	Banana 2 (contact with rotting fruit; peel intact)	Banana 3 (contact with rotting fruit; peel pierced)	Banana 4 (contact with rotting fruit; peel pierced, treated)
1				
2				
3				
4				
5				

Analyze and Conclude

1. Why were you asked to pierce the peel of the rotten banana and then use that tooth-pick to scratch the fresh bananas? What did the rotten banana represent?

_____

_____

2. At the conclusion of your observations, how did the appearance of the bananas compare? What other properties did you note? Explain your answer.

_____

_____

_____

3. Which banana was your control? How did the appearance (qualities) of the control banana change over the five days?

_____

_____

_____

4. **Error Analysis** What are some possible sources of error in your experiment?

_____

_____

5. How is the banana peel in this experiment similar to the skin on your body? What was the purpose of the rubbing alcohol?

_____

_____

_____

6. After performing this experiment, do you think it is helpful to wash and clean cuts and scrapes on your body? Explain.

_____

_____

_____

Inquiry Extensions

1. How else might you conduct this experiment? What materials would be needed?
2. Use this banana model to design an experiment to explain how hand washing can prevent the spread of the common cold virus.

Laboratory Manual

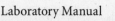

Teacher Guide and Answers

Lab 1 • Design Your Own
What makes mold grow?

Objectives
- Write a hypothesis.
- Develop an experiment to test the hypothesis.
- Control variables during the experiment.
- Draw conclusions about the formation of mold on bread.

Process Skills
design experiments, control variables, observe

Time Allotment
25 minutes the first day
5 minutes per day for the next six days

Materials
paper plates	plastic bags
dropper	(sealable)
bread (with no	tap water
preservatives)	tape

Possible Hypothesis
Mold will grow on bread that has been moistened, but not on dry bread.

Possible Procedure
1. Place two slices of bread of the same size and thickness on separate paper plates.
2. Add enough water, one drop at a time, to one slice of bread to make it just moist. Keep the other slice dry.
3. Keep both slices of bread open to the air for one hour. Then put each slice of bread into its own sealable bag. Press the outside of each bag to remove the air from the bag. Seal the bags.
4. Place a strip of tape over each seal to reinforce it.
5. Store the bags in a warm, dark place.
6. Every day, for the next five or six days, briefly remove the sealed bags from their storage place. Record whether mold has formed. Estimate the area of the bread that is covered with mold. Record this information in the data table as well.

Preparation
- Purchase several loaves of bread without preservatives a day or two before teaching the lab.
- Remind students not to eat any food in a science lab.
- Tell students not to open the sealed bags. The release of mold spores can aggravate allergies, asthma, and other medical conditions. Provide alternative activity for any students who are hypersensitive to mold spores.
- Remind students to wash their hands with soap and water at the completion of the lab.

Teaching the Lab
- Demonstrate for the students how to slide the bread off the plate and into the plastic bag.
- Encourage students to record quantitative data, such as number and size of mold colonies, and qualitative data, such as color and texture of colonies.
- Students might want to use a grid containing squares of equal size to record and estimate mold growth. A 5 × 5 grid contains 25 squares, so each grid represents approximately 4 percent of the slice.

Data and Observations
Sample data table

Mold Growth Data				
Day	Moistened Bread Slice		Unmoistened Bread Slice	
	Mold?	Area With Mold	Mold?	Area With Mold
1	No	0%	No	0%
2	Yes	15%	No	0%
3	Yes	50%	Yes	5%

Analyze and Conclude
1. The moist slice of bread became moldy. The dry slice of bread remained almost the same.
2. Mold grew on the moist bread because it had the right conditions for growth—water, food, and living space.
3. The manipulated variable was moisture. If the other variables were not controlled, it would be unclear which variable caused a specific change.
4. The control in this experiment is the slice of bread with no water. It had little or no mold growth.

Teacher Guide and Answers, continued

5. Answers will vary, but possible sources of error might include not sealing the bag tightly enough or not waiting long enough for mold to form.

6. Answers will vary, but student groups should find that factors such as moisture, heat, or darkness might aid in the growth of mold.

Write and Discuss

Student paragraphs should describe the number, size, type, and colors of mold colonies present on the moistened piece of bread. The sample hypothesis given here was supported by the data collected during the experiment.

Inquiry Extensions

1. Students should find that the bread with preservatives takes longer than the organic bread to grow mold.

2. Students should find that mold grows faster at warm temperatures and with some sunlight. Students also might want to test how long refrigerating the bread prevents mold growth, even with moisture.

Lab 2 • Design Your Own
How does your biome grow?

Objectives

- Form a hypothesis about the impact of abiotic factors on a biome.
- Design an experiment to test your hypothesis.
- Identify a control to the experiment.
- Make a model of a biome.
- Create a data table.
- Draw conclusions.

Process Skills

make models, observe, draw conclusions

Time Allotment

45 minutes the first day
5–10 minutes per day for 10 days after

Materials

bicarbonate of soda tablets	masking tape
clear plastic bottles (2-L soda bottles)	sterile potting soil
	alternative soil types (sand, clay, loam)
clear plastic wrap	
colored gels or mylar	scissors
flower seeds	small rocks
grass seeds	small beaker or test tubes
lima bean seeds	tape
index cards	water
lamps	
electric fan	

Alternative Materials

- Provide students with plant seedlings to speed up growing time.
- Clear fish bowls with glass covers can be used in place of the plastic bottles.

Possible Hypotheses

A. The abiotic factor of light wavelength will affect the growth rate of the organisms. (Students might elect to track the effect of varying the light wavelength by placing a colored gel in front of the lamp lighting the experimental biome and using a matching lamp without a gel as a control.)

B. The abiotic factor of the type of soil present in the biome will affect the growth rate of organisms. (Students can compare soil types—normal potting soil v. sandy, clay, or loamy soil.)

C. The abiotic factor of wind will affect the growth rate of organisms in a biome. (Students can create a windy climate by cutting slits or windows in the bottle and training an electric fan on the experimental biome for selected periods of the day.)

D. The abiotic factor of higher-than-normal levels of CO_2 will have a positive effect on the growth rate of organisms in a biome. (Students can dissolve a bicarbonate of soda tablet in a small beaker or test tube inside the experimental biome to increase levels of CO_2.)

E. In a temperate climate biome, the abiotic factor of water will affect the growth rate of the organisms. (A possible procedure to test this hypothesis is listed on the next page.)

Possible Procedure

1. Create mini biomes in two clear plastic bottles. Carefully cut the top ¼ off each plastic bottle. Keep in mind that the edge might be sharp—masking tape can be used to guard the edge.

2. Fill the bottles with soil to within 7.5 cm of the top.

3. Divide each soil surface into three equal sections.

4. Count out and plant the flower seeds in one section, the grass seeds in another section, and the bean seeds in the other section. (To accelerate germination, soak the seeds overnight or for a few hours before class.)

5. Initially, water the seeds in each biome well. Cover each bottle with plastic wrap.

6. Place the biomes in a location that will receive about five to six hours of direct sunlight. If this is not possible, set up a lamp, and monitor it so that the plants receive this much artificial sunlight.

7. Over the next ten days, check on the plants. Water the seeds in one of the bottles, but do not water the seeds in the other.

8. Make careful observations of the seeds, including the number of seeds that germinate, the height of the seedlings, and the number of leaves (if appropriate), and record these in the data table.

Preparation

- Have students prepare their experimental plans well in advance so that the first lab period can be devoted to constructing the biomes.

- Purchase soil and sand samples from a local garden store, or gather it in your own area.

- Make sure that there is enough space in the classroom for the lamps and the student experiments. Lamps should be connected to GFI (ground fault interrupter) outlets.

- *Impatiens* seeds and rye grass seeds work well in this lab.

Teaching the Lab

Present students with the following information about their biomes:

Biome	Soil Type	Hours of Light/Day	Watering
Forest	potting soil	1–2 h direct sunlight	let surface dry; add water
Desert	sandy soil	5–6 h direct sunlight	let soil dry to a depth of 2.5 cm below the surface
Grassland	potting soil	3–6 h direct sunlight	let surface dry, add water
Rain forest	potting soil	no direct sunlight	keep soil moist

- Students might want to look at criteria such as the number of seeds that germinate, plant height, number of leaves, color of leaves, yellowing and wilting. Ensure that students' ideas will most likely yield results.

- Encourage students to accurately measure the amount of water added to their biomes.

- Preparing plant seedlings ahead of time will speed up the length of time it takes to complete this lab.

Data and Observations

Sample data table

Model Biome Data		
Day	Biome 1 (50 mL water daily)	Biome 2 (no water)
1	no growth	no growth
2	no growth	no growth
3	sprouts— grass: 16–20 seeds sprouted; .5 mm impatiens: 5–10 seeds sprouted; 1 mm beans: 5–6 beans sprouted; .5 mm	no growth
4	sprouts—grass: .1 mm impatiens: 1.5 mm beans: 1.5 mm	no growth
5	shoots—grass: 1.2 mm impatiens: 2.4 mm with two leaves beans: 2.2 mm with two leaves	no growth
6	shoots—grass: 1.8 mm impatiens: 3.2 mm with two leaves beans: 2.5 mm with two leaves and cotyledons	no growth
7	shoots—grass: 2.2 mm impatiens: 4 mm with four leaves beans: 2.8 mm with two leaves and cotyledons	no growth
8	seedlings—grass: 2.8 mm impatiens: 4 mm with four leaves; leaves yellowing beans: 2.8 mm with two leaves and cotyledons	no growth
9	seedlings—grass: 3.3 mm impatiens: 5 mm with six leaves; some leaves green, some leaves yellowing beans: 3.5 mm with four leaves, cotyledons shriveling	no growth
10	seedlings—grass: 4.1 mm impatiens: 5.2 mm with six leaves; some leaves green, some leaves yellowing beans: 3.9 mm with four leaves, cotyledons shriveling	no growth

Teacher Guide and Answers, continued

Analyze and Conclude

1. Answers will vary. Students have choices given the materials listed above of studying the presence or absence of water, light, CO_2, or wind, as well as different soil types or different light wavelengths.

2. Answers will vary. Students will most likely find that the abiotic factor does play an important role in the biome. In the procedure outlined here, water plays a critical role in germination and growth of seedlings.

3. The bottle in which all factors remained constant serves as the control. This was done to ensure that all results were due to the manipulated variable. In the procedure cited here, the control was the bottle that received no water.

4. The abiotic factors limit the types of plants that can grow in a particular biome. The animal life in the region is determined by the plant life available.

5. Answers will vary, but students might indicate that the length of time exposed to the Sun, the amount of water, temperature, and soil type are all possible places for error.

6. Answers will vary. Students might find that the exchange leads to a new conclusion; for instance, that loamy soil is more productive despite changes in other abiotic factors, or that too much water actually inhibits germination.

7. Answers will vary. Students might recognize that there are environmental factors beyond their control, such as temperature fluctuations in the building overnight or non-viable seeds.

Write and Discuss

Student answers will vary. The paragraphs should briefly summarize the lab results and whether or not the results supported the hypothesis. Students who found that their hypothesis was incorrect, should question why the abiotic factor they selected had no apparent effect (e.g., Why didn't light levels, or wavelength, affect the speed of the beans' germination?).

Inquiry Extensions

1. Answers will vary based on the climate regions of the local area. Provide local maps and reference materials so the students can research this topic.

2. Answers will vary. Students might elect to normalize the experimental biome and see if the growth rates between it and the control biome become similar. Higher-level students might elect to change the abiotic factor based on the data they exchanged with the student in question 6 and see if the results can be replicated.

Lab 3 • Design Your Own
Do freshwater biomes respond differently to acid rain?

Objectives
- Design an experiment to assess the impact of acid rain on a freshwater pond.
- Conduct the experiment and record data.
- Interpret data and draw conclusions.

Process Skills
form hypotheses, design experiments, observe, control variables, interpret data

Time Allotment
45 minutes to set up
10 minutes per day for a week to check pH levels

Materials
pond water	large glass jars (2)
algae samples	granite gravel
limestone chips	large dropper or pipette
acid rain sample	pH test strips
light source	

Alternative Materials
- Narrow-range pH paper or a pH meter could provide more accurate readings.

Possible Hypothesis
The addition of acid rain to a pond lined with granite will kill the algae living in the pond.

Possible Procedure
1. Put 2.5–5 cm of granite gravel in the bottom of one glass jar. Leave the other glass jar with nothing on the bottom.
2. Fill each jar with pond water, ensuring that there are plenty of algae samples in the water.

Laboratory Manual

3. Measure the pH of the pond water and record this information in your data table.

4. Use a large dropper to introduce 20 mL of acid rain into each jar.

5. Use a pH strip to measure the pH of the pond water after the rain event.

6. Leave your ponds at room temperature in an area where they will receive some sunlight.

7. Measure the pH of each pond every day for a week. Record your pH values and your observations of the algae in the pond in the data table.

Preparation

• Prepare acid rain samples by adding sulfuric acid to distilled water until the pH is between 6.0 and 5.0.

• Gather pond water samples from a local pond, stream, or gardening/landscaping supplier that sells aquatic plants or pond supplies.

• Provide pure cultures of algae—closterium, spirogyra, or elodea—purchased from a supply company.

• Review the MSDS for sulfuric acid with students.

• Remind students to use GFI outlets with lamps. Using electric lamps near water presents a potential shock hazard.

Teaching the Lab

• Make sure the students' procedures make sense and will be successful.

• Students might find that the limestone buffers the effects of the acid rain. Consider assigning advanced students who have some background in chemistry to report on the solubility of calcium carbonate (limestone) in water and the properties of hard v. soft water. Calcium carbonate is not very soluble in water alone, but it does achieve some solubility in the presence of acids.

• Make sure that students have a second setup with no rocks in the bottom to see the effects of acid rain on the water.

• Encourage students to keep their ponds at room temperature in order to avoid adding another variable.

• Remind students to manipulate only one variable. For example, if they vary the gravel on the bottom of the jar (as in *Possible Procedure*), the volume of acid rain, the concentration of the acid rain, the volume of the water in the ponds, and other such factors should remain constant.

Data and Observations

Sample data table

Pond Water Data			
Day	pH of Water	Description of Algae (colors, amounts)	Other Observations
1	7.0	lots of it; most is green	acid rain water mixing with pond water
2	5.0	not as much as yesterday; slightly yellowish in color	
3	4.5	dying	

Analyze and Conclude

1. Answers will vary. Students who used granite gravel should find that the pH in their pond dropped each day as the acid content increased and spread through the water. Students who tested the pond with limestone should notice that the pH level started low and slowly rose over time.

2. Answers will vary. Students might indicate that the limestone gravel balanced the effects of the acid rain.

3. Answers will vary. Students who used the granite gravel might have found that the algae died.

4. The control in the experiment was the jar that had no gravel in the bottom. It showed the impact of the acid rain on the water alone.

5. Answers will vary, but students might note that the amount of acid rain added to the pond would impact the results. In addition, if the acid rain was added only to one side of the pond, and did not disperse, the place where the student obtained the pH sample would affect the results.

6. Answers will vary depending on the other groups' setups. Students should conclude that the presence of limestone buffers the effects of acid rain, while life in ponds that have granite at their base are more vulnerable to changes in pH caused by acid rain.

Write and Discuss

Students might find that their hypotheses were supported. If they had some background information regarding the properties of limestone, they might have been familiar with its neutralizing capabilities.

Teacher Guide and Answers, continued

Inquiry Extensions

1. Students might find that higher temperatures cause the pH of a sample to increase.
2. Students should discuss how acid rain can impact their lives by destroying the life of favorite fishing spots, disrupting life at favorite vacation locations, and potentially disrupting aquatic systems in food webs and food chains, which could potentially impact the human food chain.

Lab 4 • Classic
How can you show a population trend?

Objectives
- Culture bacterial colonies to track population growth.
- Graph population data, choosing appropriate scales and titles.
- Compare and contrast populations and the factors that affect growth.

Process Skills
graph, compare and contrast, make inferences

Time Allotment
30 minutes to set up plates
10–15 minutes two days later

Materials
pieces of graph paper (4)   petri dishes
ruler   with lids (2)
pencil   nutrient agar
eraser   masking tape
calculator   permanent marker
colored pencils

Alternative Materials
- computer
- graphing program

Preparation
- Set up your own culture plate to run concurrently with the students'. This way, if their samples do not grow a culture of bacteria, they can refer to yours.

- Introduce the students to the different types of population graphs they might encounter in this exercise. This would include *J*-graphs, *S*-graphs, and exponential growth graphs.
- Remind students to always wash their hands after handling their inoculated petri dishes.
- Petri dishes recently removed from the autoclave might be hot.
- Confirm that students do not use cracked or compromised plates.
- Make sure you account for all cultured plates, as well as their adequate disposal.

Teaching the Lab
- A pressure cooker or autoclave is needed to sterilize the growth chamber.
- Sterilize the growth chambers for 15 min at pressure 1 bar or 6.8 kg/2.5 cm^2.
- Growth chambers can also be created using paper cups, wax paper, aluminum foil, and raw potato.
- Encourage students to use the rulers to make sure they are lining up the numbers on the graphs properly.
- Remind students to choose their vertical and horizontal axes carefully and to choose appropriate scales. Circulate around the room to help direct students.

Data and Observations
Sample data and graphs
Sample data for Table 1

Bacterial Growth	
Petri Dish	Number of Colonies/ Percentage of Surface Covered
(A) Control	0-1 colonies
(B) Contaminated	28 colonies

Graph for data from Table 2

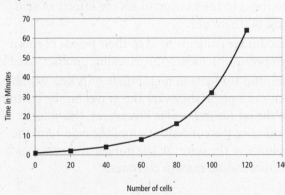

Laboratory Manual

Graph for data from Table 3

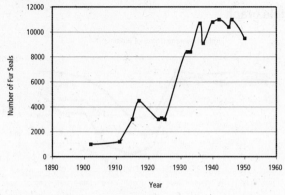

Year

Graph for data from Table 4

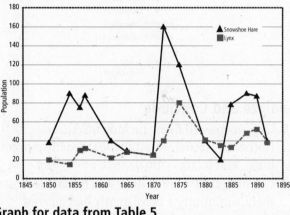

Year

Graph for data from Table 5

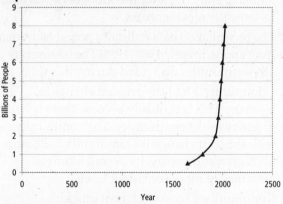

Year

Analyze and Conclude

1. Students should understand that the agar contains nutrients on which the bacteria can feed.

2. Conditions are not always right for bacterial growth. Light, food supply, humidity, and temperature are among the factors that need to be at certain levels in order to be conducive for bacterial growth. Even though small numbers of bacteria may be on numerous objects in our environment, in general, conditions are not right for large, visible colonies to form.

3. The curve for the growth of bacteria is a *J*-curve. The curve gets steeper as the rate of growth increases.

4. Lack of bacteria from inoculant might be a cause for error, as well as inhospitable culturing conditions (e.g., plates were too cold).

5. The fur seal population data best fits on an *S*-curve. The population starts off slow, shows a relatively rapid increase, and then levels off at the end.

6. As the seal population grew, the animals might have reached a limiting factor, such as space. This means that there were too many animals competing for the same resources. This caused the population's niche to reach its carrying capacity, and population growth started to level off. The number of animals had reached a level where it used as many resources as were available, so the population stabilized.

7. The hare and the lynx follow a similar pattern. The peaks and declines of each population seem to closely mirror each other.

8. The hare and the lynx have a predator-prey relationship. The lynx preys on the hare, so an increase in the lynx population eventually means a decrease in the hare population. As the hare population decreases, the lynx population also eventually decreases. This decrease in the lynx population will eventually lead to an increase in the hare population, and the cycle will start over.

9. The human population exploded in number and is increasing at a rapid rate. This has caused concern because Earth eventually will reach its carrying capacity, and the human population will start to level off, just like the population of the fur seal.

Inquiry Extensions

1. Answers will vary. Students should recognize that medicine and technology generally increase the life span of humans, contributing to the population growth.

2. Other predator-prey relationships might include owls and field mice, hawks and snakes, or bears and salmon. Students should see a trend similar to the lynx-hare trend that they observed in this exercise.

Lab 5 • Classic
How do we measure biodiversity?

Objectives
- Analyze data from four test sites.
- Infer trends in biodiversity.
- Predict what environmental factors impact biodiversity.

Process Skills
graph, model, infer, predict, draw conclusions

Time Allotment
45 minutes

Materials
pen   colored pencils
graph paper   calculator
ruler

Alternative Materials
- You might want students to graph the data using a computer and graphing program.

Preparation
- Make sure you have enough graph paper for each student
- Review graphing techniques with students if necessary.

Teaching the Lab
- Make sure students choose appropriate scales for their graph.
- Explain that each of the farms has been abandoned and then left undisturbed. Secondary succession is slowly returning each site to its natural habitat.
- Assist students in their understanding of how the original data was collected. The average of grams of biomass per site was determined by collecting, drying, and measuring the mass of all the plant material that could be clipped from a 0.3-m^2 area. The study was done over the course of 11 years at the Cedar Creek Natural History Area just north of the Minneapolis-St. Paul metropolitan area. The natural disaster of a drought during 1987–1988 provided an unusual opportunity to measure biomass effects and recovery in the area.

Data and Observations
Sample graph

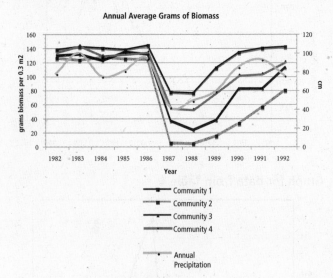

Annual Average Grams of Biomass

Analyze and Conclude
1. Organisms will likely include field grasses (forbes or weeds), small shrubs, rodents, insects, birds, and larger animals such as coyotes.
2. Community 1 is most diverse. The data indicate that Community 1 consistently had greater biomass, and even after the drought, it was able to show the most biomass.
3. The precipitation data indicate a period of drought from approximately 1987–1989. The biodiversity in all communities decreased during this time.
4. Community 2 had the greatest change in biomass. This is probably because there is less diversity in the community. The community with the least change is Community 1. Because of its greater diversity, its overall biomass remained at more consistent levels.
5. Community 1 recovered most quickly. Community 2 recovered most slowly.
6. Inability to analyze the data presented could be a source of error.
7. It appears that the greater the diversity and the more biomass in a community, the more stable it is.

Inquiry Extensions
1. Students could cite events such as fire, flooding, or disease invasion as factors. Their predictions should show the greatest impact on and slowest recovery in Community 2. Communities with the

     Laboratory Manual

most diverse biomass would rebound faster because the soil has more nutrients to support new growth.

2. Students could design an experiment in which an affected area is examined over a period of time. Real-estate development would adversely affect biodiversity. In addition to loss of biomass, students could mention habitat destruction, changes in water runoff patterns, or wind erosion. Because three of the communities were once farms, students might try to analyze the impact of fertilizers and pesticides. Human impact in the form of conservation efforts could result in more rapid naturalization through selected species re-introduction, protection for water, or removal of litter and pollutants.

Lab 6 • Design Your Own
How much vitamin C are you getting?

Objectives
- Make predictions about the amounts of vitamin C in a variety of drinks.
- Design an experiment to compare the amounts of vitamin C in these beverages.
- Measure how different substances react in the presence of iodine.
- Draw conclusions about the nutritional value of the beverages.

Process Skills
measure, make predictions, design an experiment, draw conclusions, use titration as a testing method

Materials
50-mL beakers (6)
plastic droppers
starch solution
tincture of iodine
vitamin-C solution
orange juice
juices and sports drinks with added vitamin C (4)
(Note: Because the students will be looking for a blue-purple color change, do not provide drinks that are dark in color.)
envelope containing copies of nutritional information labels keyed to each drink, to be distributed after the students complete the procedure

Alternative Materials
- Any type of juice or sports drink that makes a claim about vitamin-C content can be used.

Possible Hypothesis
Orange juice has the most vitamin C; therefore, a sample of orange juice will require the most drops of iodine to observe a reaction with the starch.

Possible Procedure
1. Choose five beverages to test. Predict which one has the highest level of vitamin C and which has the lowest. Rank each sample according to the prediction.
2. Create a data table to record this information.
3. Set out and label six 50-mL beakers. In the first beaker, place 25 mL of vitamin-C solution. Add 25 mL of each beverage to its own beaker.
4. Add two drops of starch solution to each beaker.
5. Beginning with the vitamin-C solution, add one drop of iodine to the beaker, and gently swirl. Observe any change. Continue to add the iodine, one drop at a time, until the liquid turns a dark blue color. Record the number of iodine drops needed to form this color.
6. Repeat step 5 for the beverages in the remaining five beakers.

Preparation
- Prepare the starch solution by directing a stream of spray starch into 75–100 mL of water in a beaker while stirring rapidly. A mixture at the correct strength will have a pale blue tinge.
- Tincture of iodine, which is used as a skin antiseptic, works well. Use a brand that comes with a dropper.
- Prepare a 1-percent ascorbic-acid solution. [See Preparation of Solutions, pp. T13–T15.]
- Small containers of beverages will provide enough samples for a class.
- Choose a variety of juices and sports or energy drinks that students might be familiar with or drink on a daily basis. This will make the experiment more interesting for them.

Teaching the Lab

- Demonstrate how to add iodine one drop at a time and how to gently swirl the cup.
- Make sure that students remember to add the starch solution to each beaker; otherwise, the color-change reaction will not take place.
- After students have completed the procedure, distribute the copies of the nutritional labels. Students will compare their results with the information provided on the labels. Have them assess if the information supports their results. In addition, provide this information on the board:
  - The Recommended Dietary Allowance (RDA) for vitamin C is 90 mg/day for adult males and 75 mg/day for adult women.
  - There are 64 mg of vitamin C in 125 mL of orange juice.

Data and Observations

Sample data table

Vitamin C Data			
Beverage	Drops of Iodine	Predicted Ranking	Actual Ranking
Vitamin-C solution	9	control	control
Orange juice	6	1	2
Apple juice	2	5	3
White cranberry juice	2	4	4
Yellow energy drink	1	2	5
Green sports drink	10	3	1

Analyze and Conclude

1. Answers will vary based on the samples analyzed in class. Orange juice usually has a high concentration of vitamin C, while apple juice usually has a low concentration, unless it is fortified.
2. Answers will vary depending on samples. The amount of vitamin C present in the beverage determines the outcome of the test, whether it is naturally occurring or added by a manufacturer.
3. In general, higher levels of vitamin C provide greater nutritional value.
4. The students should use the vitamin-C solution as a control. It will show the maximum number of drops of iodine needed to cause a reaction.

5. Students might cite miscounting the iodine drops or not observing when the solution changed color as possible sources of error. The iodine drops themselves might not be identical in volume, which could also create variance among the samples being tested. In addition, the age of the sample and exposure to oxygen might have degraded the vitamin C.
6. Depending on the beverages chosen for the samples, there will be a wide range of answers to this question. Generally, orange juice will have the highest percentage of vitamin C per serving among drinks not fortified with vitamin C. Some of the drinks fortified with vitamin C might offer 100 percent of the RDA per serving.

Write and Discuss

Students who submitted the hypothesis stating that the highest concentration of vitamin C would be found in orange juice will find their hypothesis supported (unless a juice/drink with extra-high amounts of vitamin C was made available for the test). Students should restate the rankings their tests showed.

Inquiry Extensions

1. Students should find that the vitamin-C content decreases as the expiration date passes or if the juice is left exposed to the air.
2. Because hydrochloric acid is the stomach's primary digestive agent, students should design an experiment that uses the same tests as in the main lab but should add HCl to the orange juice before starting. Test results should show that vitamin-C availability is comparable to the original test results, indicating that HCl does not affect the vitamin's bioavailablity.

Lab 7 • Design Your Own
What substances or solutions act as buffers?

Objectives

- Form a hypothesis about the success of certain materials as buffers.
- Design an experiment to test your hypothesis.
- Control the variables in your experiments.
- Draw conclusions about the success of animal and plant solutions as buffers in biological systems.

Process Skills

control variables, form hypotheses, design experiments, draw conclusions

Time Allotment

45 minutes

Materials

pH meter	liver solution
stirring rod	egg solution
50-mL beaker	gelatin solution
500-mL beaker	fruit solution
50-mL graduated	cucumber solution
cylinder	buffer 7
0.1M HCl	water
0.1M NaOH	

Alternative Materials

- If a pH probe is not available, specific-range pH strips can be substituted. However, the data they provide might not be as accurate.

Possible Hypothesis

Materials made of animal tissues will be the best buffers, then plant tissues, then water.

Possible Procedure

1. Set up a beaker of rinse water by pouring 200–300 mL in the 500-mL beaker.
2. Pour 25 mL of distilled water into a 50-mL beaker.
3. Measure the pH of the water, and record this figure in the data table.
4. Return the pH meter to the rinse water.
5. Add five drops of HCl to the water. Use the stirring rod to stir the liquid.
6. Retest the pH, and record this information in the data table. Rinse the pH meter.
7. Add five more drops of HCl to the water.
8. Repeat steps 6 and 7.
9. Continue repeating steps 7 and 8 until you have added a total of 30 drops of HCl.
10. Repeat steps 2-9 with the NaOH. Be sure to rinse the probe each time.
11. Rinse all the beakers and repeat testing with HCl and NaOH with the remaining solutions (liver, egg, gelatin, cucumber, or fruit), including buffer 7.

Preparation

- Prepare solutions of animal and plant tissue. For the animal source, blend about 0.113 kg of fresh or frozen liver with 500–600 mL of water. For the plant source, blend one cucumber or other fruit with 500–600 mL water.
- Make sure that the gelatin is liquid and not firm.
- Buffer 7 is available commercially or can be made. [See Preparation of Solutions, pp. T13–T15.]
- Use care with HCl and NaOH solutions.

Teaching the Lab

- Review with students the procedure for using the pH meter. Remind them to hold the pH meter upright and read it when the number has become steady.
- Emphasize the importance of rinsing the pH meter after each use.
- Remind students that gelatin is an animal product.

Data and Observations

Sample data table

pH of Solution							
Solution	Drops of HCl						
	0	5	10	15	20	25	30
Water	7.0	6.0	3.3	2.8	2.6	2.5	2.4
Liver	6.6	6.3	5.9	6.0	5.3	5.2	5.2
Fruit	4.8	4.7	4.4	4.2	3.7	3.7	3.6
Egg	9.5	9.3	9.0	8.5	8.2	7.9	7.6
Gelatin	6.0	5.0	4.5	3.9	3.5	3.2	3.0
Cucumber	6.7	6.4	5.9	5.8	5.4	5.2	5.1
Buffer	7.2	7.1	7.1	7.1	7.1	7.1	7.1

pH of Solution							
Solution	Drops of NaOH						
	0	5	10	15	20	25	30
Water	7.0	9.1	9.5	9.7	9.9	10.0	10.1
Liver	6.6	6.7	6.8	6.9	6.8	7.3	7.9
Fruit	4.8	5.2	6.0	6.2	6.6	7.3	7.9
Egg	9.5	9.7	9.8	9.9	10.1	10.1	10.2
Gelatin	6.0	6.9	7.9	9.0	9.5	9.7	10.0
Cucumber	6.7	7.1	7.2	7.4	7.8	8.1	8.5
Buffer	7.2	7.1	7.1	7.1	7.1	7.1	7.1

Analyze and Conclude

1. Answers will vary, but students should find that the animal solutions were the most effective buffers and the water was the least effective.

2. Students should have found that the buffering ability of water was not good.

3. The solutions made from animal products were best. The results of the experiment showed that the liver was the most effective buffer of the animal products. The liver lost only 1.4 pH points with the highest amount of acid, and gained only 1.3 with the greatest amount of base. The fruit was a much better buffer of the acid (net loss 1.4 pH) than of the base (net gain 3.1 pH).

4. The control in this experiment was measuring the pH of the water before drops were added. The control showed what happens when acid or base is added to solution in which no buffering occurs.

5. Answers will vary, but students will probably indicate that forgetting to rinse the pH meter, an inaccurate reading on the meter, or miscounting the drops were possible sources of error.

6. Answers will vary, but, in general, the other groups should have found that the animal products were the most effective buffers.

Write and Discuss

Answers will vary. Students might be surprised to find that animal tissue makes the best buffer. They might find that their experiment raises questions about cases in real life where buffers are needed, such as when increased respiration causes a change in blood pH, or when there are external sources of pH change such as acid rain.

Inquiry Extensions

1. Answers will vary. Student research should uncover that it is relatively easy to alter blood pH level. For example hyperventilation which leads to alkalosis (pH is too high). Other conditions or diseases that can lead to alkalosis are fever, anxiety, high environmental temperature, or pulmonary embolus. The opposite state of blood pH, acidosis (pH is too low), can result from airway obstruction, acute respiratory infections, starvation, or certain complications of diabetes. The best student public service announcements will present causes, symptoms, and rememdies.

2. The body has three important buffering systems— the phosphate buffer system, the protein buffer system, and the bicarbonate buffer system which is the primary buffering system at work in the blood. Each system works on a molecular level to take up or donate hydrogen ions in solution, helping to bring the overall solution back to a near-neutral pH.

   In the phosphate buffer, phosphoric acid changes into dihydrogen phosphate when it gives up a hydrogen ion. Dihydrogen phosphate can lose one more ion and become monohydrogen phosphate, or take an ion back, returning to phosphoric acid.

   In the protein buffer, an amino acid's carboxyl group can take on extra hydrogen ions in the presence of acid, while its amino group can release hydrogen ions in the presence of a base.

   In the bicarbonate buffer, a bicarbonate ion in the presence of acid can accept ahydrogen ion and become a carbonic ion. Conversely, in the presence of a base, a bicarbonate ion will give up a hydrogen ion, becoming carbonic acid.

Lab 8 • Classic
Why do cells divide?

Objectives
- Model cells of different sizes with agar cubes.
- Model the diffusion of materials across a cell membrane.
- Calculate the surface area-to-volume ratio for model cells.
- Form a hypothesis about how cell division affects a cell's ability to absorb materials.

Process Skills
make models, control variables, draw conclusions

Time Allotment
45 minutes

Materials
agar, prepared with phenolpthalein	100 mL 0.1*M* solution of hydrochloric acid
beaker	kitchen knife
timer	plastic spoons
calculator	paper towels
plastic ruler	

Alternative Materials
- plain gelatin prepared with food coloring

Preparation
- Prepare agar with phenophthalein. [See Preparation of Solutions, pp. T13–T15.]
- Cut the agar cubes ahead of time to save time.
- Write the math formulas on the board for students to see.
- Review MSDS for hydrochloric acid with students.

Teaching the Lab
- Review basic math techniques with the students as needed.
- Students should use gloves when measuring the agar cubes that have been exposed to the hydrochloric acid solution.

Data and Observations
Sample data table

Agar Cube Data				
Cube Size	Surface Area	Volume	Ratio	Depth of Diffusion
3 cm/side	54 cm³	27 cm³	2	
2 cm/side	24 cm³	8 cm³	3	
1 cm/side	6 cm³	1 cm³	6	

Analyze and Conclude
1. No, it is greatest in the block with the largest surface area-to-volume ratio.
2. No, it does not seem to be the same. Factors such as size can affect it.
3. The largest cube has the smallest surface area-to-volume ratio.
4. 600
5. The onion cube has the greatest surface area-to-volume ratio.
6. The depth of diffusion increases as the surface area-to-volume ratio increases.
7. The depth of diffusion decreases as a cell grows larger.
8. Answers will vary, but students might explain that their method of cutting the agar or measuring the distances of diffusion might be sources of error.
9. Answers will vary. As cell growth continues, it becomes more difficult for a cell to get all the materials it needs. When a cell reaches the maximum size at which it can effectively take in enough nutrients, it must divide or die.

Inquiry Extensions
1. Epithelial cells in the stomach and intestines live, die, and are replaced about every two days. Because of the highly acidic environment of the stomach, its cells are rapidly "burned out" and need to be replaced. Some neural cells never replicate themselves, but recent research has shown that mental and physical exercise can stimulate the growth of new neurons. Inactivity, starvation, and inhospitable temperatures are all candidates for slowing or stopping division in certain cells.

2. Answers will vary. Students should understand that the demands of rapid growth will cause more and faster cell division and a concurrent demand for more nutrients. Higher-level students might relate these new physical demands to the occurrence in human adolescents of "growing pains" and significantly increased appetite.

Lab 9 • Design Your Own
How many calories do different foods contain?

Objectives
- Identify foods to test.
- Assemble a simple calorimeter.
- Design an experiment to test a hypothesis.
- Draw conclusions about available energy in food.

Process Skills
design an experiment, infer, calculate, measure

Time Allotment
two 45-minute periods

Materials
metal coffee can (clean; open at both ends)	food samples such as rice cakes, peanuts, dried beans, dried cheese, marshmallows
metal soup can (clean; must fit inside the coffee can)	temperature probe or thermometer
cork	matches
straight pins or dissecting pins	candles
aluminum foil	locking tongs
test-tube holder	dissecting probe
graduated cylinder	weigh boats
masking tape	scale

Alternative Materials
- Bunsen burners
- A paper clip can be bent into a basket to hold the food samples.

Possible Hypothesis
A high-fat food, such as cheese, will have a much higher calorie content than foods lower in fat, such as beans.

Possible Procedure
1. Set up a calorimeter as follows. Place the coffee can on the table. Suspend the soup can from the top of the coffee can. Support with tongs if necessary.
2. Add 100 mL of water to the soup can. Take a baseline temperature measurement.
3. Choose one food item to test. Weigh it on the balance, and record this measurement in the data table.
4. Carefully place the point of the pin into the food so that it is secure. Place the pin in the cork.
5. Using extreme caution, touch a lit candle to the food until it is burning on its own.
6. Carefully place the apparatus over the burning food.

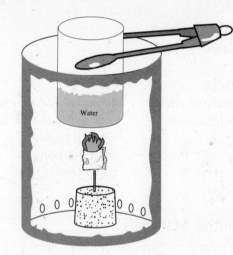

7. Use a temperature probe to record the temperature in the water every 20 s. Record your answer in degrees Celsius. Place the probe in the water but not touching the sides of the soup can.
8. After burning is complete, record the highest temperature reached.
9. Remove the ash from the pin, and weigh what remains.
10. Subtract the end mass from the beginning mass, and record this information.
11. Determine the change in temperature.
12. Determine the number of calories in the food and the number of calories per gram.

Preparation
- Do not use peanuts in this lab if there is any history of nut allergies in the class or in your school. Dried beans or soy nuts will work fine.

Teacher Guide and Answers, continued

- Cut a block of marble jack cheese into 7-mm cubes. Allow the cheese to dry on several layers of paper towel for about a month. In order to mount a cube on the pin, the students might soften the cheese in the flame or heat the probe and poke a hole in the cheese.
- Cut vent holes in the lower portion of the coffee can.
- Have food samples on hand. These might include dried cheese, beans, nuts, rice cakes, or dried vegetables.
- Students can use the dissecting probe to make a hole in the cork that is large enough for the head of the straight pin. Or, push a large dissecting pin through the bottom of a piece of cork that has been covered in three layers of aluminum foil.
- Caution students that the metal tongs and inner can might become hot to the touch. Use hot pads or mitts to avoid burns.

Teaching the Lab
- Remind students not to eat anything in this lab.
- Consider setting up a calorimeter before class so students can use it as a model.
- Remind students to use caution when lighting their samples.
- Have students check the distance from the top of the sample to the bottom of the soup can *before* they light the food sample.

Data and Observations
Sample data table

Calorie Data		
Sample	Rice Cake	Dried Cheese
Beginning weight	0.861 g	0.59 g
End weight	0.198 g	.018 g
Weight change	0.663 g	0.49 g
Water volume	100.0 ml	100.0 ml
Beginning temperature	20.1°C	22.9°C
End temperature	26.9°C	30.0°C
Temperature change	+6.8°C	+7.1°C
Calories	680	710
Calories per gram	1025.6	1448.98

Analyze and Conclude
1. Answers will vary depending on the foods tested. Students should find that foods high in fat, such as nuts or cheese, are higher in calories. Vegetables and rice are lower in calories.
2. Answers will vary, but the amount of available energy is greater in foods high in fats and sugars.
3. The differences in calories are due to the differences in fat and sugar in the foods.
4. Answers will vary. Sample definition: Cellular energy is measured by the amount of calories in a food.
5. All of the available energy did not go into the water because this calorimeter is not a closed system. Some of the heat escaped through and around the side of the can.
6. Answers will vary. Students might recognize that measuring the temperature accurately could be a source of error.
7. Animals store fat because it is a condensed form of energy which is not soluble in water, while plants—which do not have to move around—can store starch. Starch is bulkier, but it is soluble in water.

Write and Discuss
Students whose hypotheses stated that foods higher in fat (and, secondarily, protein) have the highest calories per gram will have their hypotheses supported by the data.

Inquiry Extensions
1. Accept all reasonable experimental designs. Students should find that the addition of sugar will speed up the rate of fermentation. Students might also find that an increase in temperature will do the same, but if the temperature is raised too high, the yeast will die.
2. Accept all reasonable experimental designs. Students should find that hardwoods burn cleaner and hotter (with more calories released) than softer woods. The example with the different types of coal should show that lignite burns least efficiently and anthracite burns most efficiently. Advanced learners might mention that burning lignite coal produces undesirable levels of mercury emissions, while anthracite emissions tend to be cleaner.

Lab 10 • Design Your Own
What can affect the rate of photosynthesis?

Objectives
- Formulate a hypothesis about the connection between light intensity and oxygen production in photosynthesis.
- Design an experiment to test this hypothesis.
- Control variables, and use a control during the experiment.
- Draw a conclusion about the rate of photosynthesis.

Process Skills
formulate hypotheses, design experiments, control variables, draw conclusions

Time Allotment
30 minutes to set up
20 minutes the next day for observations

Materials
large glass jars (3)	test tubes (3)
aged tap water	lamp
baking soda (sodium bicarbonate)	medium to large box lined with white paper
scale	
Elodea samples	medium to large box lined with gray paper
ruler	
scissors	
small glass funnels (3)	

Alternative Materials
- Yew (evergreen) can be used successfully in place of the *Elodea.*

Possible Hypothesis
Light with higher intensity (or brighter light) will produce oxygen through photosynthesis at a faster rate.

Possible Procedure
1. Fill three jars with aged water. Add 1g of sodium bicarbonate to each jar.
2. Obtain three *Elodea* samples from aquaria shops or biological supply houses. Cut off the lower part of the stems.

3. Rub the upper 2.5 cm of each stem between your fingers to crush it.
4. Place an *Elodea* sample in each jar, and cover it with a funnel. Make sure that the crushed portion is pointing up.

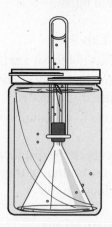

5. Fill a test tube with water. Place your index finger over the mouth of the test tube, and invert it over the spout of the funnel. Do not let any water escape from the test tube. Do not remove your finger until the mouth of the test tube is completely under water.
6. Place one jar inside the box lined with white paper. Aim a bright lamp into the box so that the light can reflect off the paper but the heat from the bulb can escape. Allow the plant to receive bright light for 24 h.
7. Place the second jar in the box with gray paper so that it receives dim light for 24 h.
8. Place a third jar in the dark for 24 h.
9. After 24 h, measure the height of the gas collected in the test tubes. Record the data in the data table.

Teacher Guide and Answers, continued

Preparation
- Leave several gallons of tap water uncovered in the classroom overnight to age. This will allow the chlorine in the water to dissipate or "gas-off," making the water more hospitable to aquatic plants.
- Make sure that the mouths of the jars are wide enough to allow the student's hand to fit inside while holding a test tube.
- Have enough fresh *Elodea* samples for each group to have three samples.
- Remind students not to taste, eat, or drink any materials used in the lab.
- Use extreme caution when operating the electric lights near water. Place the electric lamps in the light boxes, then move the water-filled jars into position. If possible, use only ground fault circuit interruption (GFCI) protected outlets.

Teaching the Lab
- Make sure that students do not let water escape from the test tube as they invert it. Tell them that if some of the water leaks out they should start over.
- Use gooseneck lamps with a 150-watt bulb. Training the lamps into the boxes will provide light for the plants, but make sure to limit heat gain in the water, which would cause an undesirable result.
- Check each student's experimental design to make sure that there are bubbles forming at the cut end. If not, have the student start over with a fresher piece of plant.

Data and Observations
Sample data table

Gas Production of Elodea Samples	
Location	Height of Gas Column (cm)
Bright light	0.8
Dim light	0.4
Dark	0.1

Analyze and Conclude
1. The plant that received the most light produced the most oxygen.
2. There is no proof that it is oxygen. One way to test it could be to insert a glowing wooden splint into the inverted test tube.
3. Sodium bicarbonate provided an additional source of carbon dioxide needed for photosynthesis.
4. The greater the light intensity, the more gas produced. This gas is what was seen in the data.
5. The control in this experiment was the plant placed in the dark. This control showed that little, if any, photosynthesis can occur in the absence of light.
6. Answers will vary, but students should report that removing their fingers from the test tube too soon or the availability of light could be sources of error. Additionally, heat from a lamp that causes the water temperature to rise would create an undesirable result.
7. Answers will vary, as students might have tested different types of lighting situations. Students should find that as more light is made available to the plant, more oxygen is produced.

Write and Discuss
Students should report that for this particular plant, light with greater intensity led to greater oxygen production.

Inquiry Extensions
1. Students should find that there is a difference in the daily amount of oxygen released by photosynthesis. They should then infer that the amount of oxygen entering the atmosphere would be less during the long winter nights.
2. Students should predict that organisms dependent on free oxygen, either in the air or in the water, would die out if plants disappeared. Except for species that thrive in high-heat, high-pressure underwater environments, and anaerobic bacteria that are not dependent on aerobic organisms, life on Earth depends on plants for food and on the oxygen plants produce. The decline of animal life would be quick, not allowing animals time to adapt to the changes in the atmosphere. Students should also discover that the bulk of the oxygen is produced by the phytoplankton in the ocean and not by terrestrial plants.

Lab 11 • Classic
How long does each phase of the cell cycle last?

Objectives
- Use a microscope to identify cells in an onion root tip.
- Identify the different stages of the cell cycle in onion cells.
- Count the number of cells in each stage of the cell cycle.
- Calculate the amount of time cells spend in each stage of the cell cycle.

Process Skills
observe, calculate, interpret data

Time Allotment
45 minutes

Materials
microscope
colored pencils
calculator
prepared slide of onion root tip cells undergoing cell division

Alternative Materials
If you have an additional lab period to devote to this exploration, the students could prepare the slides themselves using real onion cells. This would require:
- cover slips
- onions
- scalpels
- slides
- Feulgen stain
- water

Preparation
- Ensure that each phase of the cell cycle is well represented on the prepared slides.
- Provide students with pictures of each phase of the cell cycle so they can easily identify them under the microscope.
- Remind students to handle the slides carefully to prevent breakage or injury.
- Duplicate copies of **Table 1** for the students' use.

Teaching the Lab
- Most of the cells students count should be in the interphase stage of the cell cycle, but errors in counting and differences in samples might give varying results.
- Circulate around the room to ensure that students are observing what they need to.
- Review basic microscope skills for those students who might need it.

Data and Observations
Table 1

Cell Cycle Data							
Stage	Description	Tally Marks	Your Total	Class Total	Total	Percent of Total	Time of Stage
Interphase	nucleus without distinctly visible chromosomes; nucleolus often visible as a dot or two		43	46	89	89%	641 min
Prophase	chromosome material visible but scattered through the nucleus; nuclear membrane dissolving		3	4	7	7%	50 min
Metaphase	chromosomes gathered at the middle of the cell		1	1	2	2%	14 min
Anaphase	chromosomes definitely moving toward opposite ends of the cell, might even be reaching the poles		1	0	1	1%	7 min
Telophase	two tiny cells next to each other; nucleus is not solid looking yet		0	1	1	1%	7 min

Analyze and Conclude
1. Most students will notice more cells in interphase.
2. DNA replication and, by extension, nuclear division have to take place before mitosis can begin.
3. Answers will vary. Students might note that there is more activity in some stages than in others or that the cell could be spending more time in one stage to develop further. For instance, students might be able to observe activities such as the nuclear membrane dissolving, centrioles moving into place, and the chromatin raveling.

4. Interphase is the longest phase. And prophase appears to be the longest phase in mitosis. Anaphase and telophase are minor stages.

5. In the case of a plant cell, telophase ends with the appearance of the cell plate. Cytokinesis is complete when a new cell wall separates the daughter cells, and they enter interphase.

6. Answers might vary, but students should recognize that many of their errors can come from either miscounting or misidentifying the stages.

7. The cell cycle can be explained as multiplying by dividing because in order to make new cells—to multiply in number—the cells must divide.

Inquiry Extensions

1. Allow students to conduct their experiments to test their hypothesis. Have prepared animal slides available for them to count. If the centrioles appear during prophase in an animal cell, this might make this stage the most significant and longest.

2. The cell cycle occurs in all living things. Mitosis occurs in an accelerated form during growth phases, injury repair, and during certain diseases such as cancer. All of these relate to the adolescent learner and make the cell cycle directly applicable.

Lab 12 • Design Your Own
Green or yellow?

Objectives
- Develop a hypothesis to predict the impact sunlight will have on the phenotypes of flowering tobacco seedlings.
- Design an experiment to test this hypothesis.
- Identify a control in the experiment.
- Draw conclusions from the plants that grow.

Process Skills
develop hypotheses; design an experiment; identify differences; infer causes, states, or conditions; draw conclusions

Time Allotment
45 minutes to set up
5 minutes per day until the seeds sprout and show their colors

Materials
Nicotiana alata (flowering tobacco) seeds
filter paper
petri dishes
fine-point permanent marker
water
sunny spot in the room
dark corner in the room
metric ruler

Alternative Materials
- Water in a spray bottle can be used to keep the filter paper moist.

Possible Hypothesis
The plant leaves that receive sunlight will be green, but the plant leaves that grow in the dark will be yellow.

Possible Procedure
1. Write the names of your group members on four sheets of filter paper and moisten them with water. Set each piece of filter paper in a petri dish.
2. Place ten tobacco seeds on each sheet of damp filter paper.
3. Choose a spot in the classroom where there is direct sunlight for part of the day. Place one of your filter paper squares in that spot.
4. Choose another spot in the room that receives indirect sunlight for most of the day but no direct sunlight. Place one of your filter paper squares in that spot.
5. Choose a location in the classroom where the seeds will grow in the dark. Place one of your filter paper squares in the location.
6. Choose a location in the room where there is no sunlight but where you are able to set up a lamp. Place your last filter paper square under the light. This will act as your control.
7. Check the seeds daily. Moisten as needed.
8. Wash hands with soap and water after each lab.

Preparation
- Order the tobacco seeds in advance of this laboratory exercise. You will want to find seeds that have a 3:1 green to yellow ratio. Do not get albino seeds.

- Clear the counters, windowsills, and the closet in your classroom to ensure students will have enough room to set up their experiments.
- Caution students to watch for mold growth on wet filter paper or seeds. Discard if mold is present.

Teaching the Lab

- This lab will work well with groups of four students.
- Make sure students have a control included in their experimental plan.
- Although the color of the leaves is the most obvious phenotypical difference, students might note other differences, such as height or number of leaves.

Data and Observations

Sample data table

Impact of Light on Plants			
Location	Number of Seeds	Phenotypes of Seeds	Ratio of Green to Yellow
Sunny windowsill	10	green and yellow	3:1
Table with indirect sunlight	10	green and yellow	3:1
Closet	10	yellow	0:10
Behind the fume hood with a lamp	10	green and yellow	3:1

Analyze and Conclude

1. No green plants grew in the dark. In the sunlight, three green plants grew for every one yellow plant.
2. In this scenario, the environmental factor of direct sunlight directly affected the phenotypes of these plants.
3. Possible answers include the exposure to sunlight activated the chlorophyll in the plants.
4. The control was a set of seeds that were grown with no sunlight but in artificial light.
5. Possible sources of error might include some direct sunlight reaching the seeds that are meant to be kept in the dark, or the seeds not receiving enough water or nutrients.
6. Answers will vary. Most of the other groups should have observed the same ratio.

Write and Discuss

Students whose hypothesis stated that there would be a difference in the expression of the phenotype should have had their hypothesis supported by the experiment. The ratio of green to yellow seedlings (3:1), however, would have been difficult to predict without prior knowledge.

Inquiry Extensions

1. Accept all reasonable experimental designs. Students might want to test the impact temperature, soil types, or food has on the plants.
2. Quantitative measurements of the yellow seedlings should show them to be nearly identical to the green seedlings in terms of height, weight, and number of leaves.

Lab 13 • Classic
What are the chances?

Objectives

- Construct a pedigree for a family.
- Determine the probability of a couple having a child with the genetic disorder.

Process Skills

interpret data, predict

Time Allotment

45 minutes

Possible Materials

index cards (two colors—blue and pink)
scissors
pencil

Alternative Materials

- plain white index cards

Preparation

- To save time, cut the index cards before beginning the class.
- Draw a pedigree showing the family relationships ahead of time for the students to use to check their work before continuing with the rest of the lab.
- If time allows, prepare pedigrees of other inherited diseases to show to students.

Teaching the Lab

- Be sensitive to the personal history of the students in class. Some students or their family members might suffer from a genetic disorder.
- Allow the students to check their pedigree against yours so they are sure it is correct before they proceed.
- Remind students that they might have to draw a Punnett square to answer some of the questions.

Data and Observations

Sample pedigree

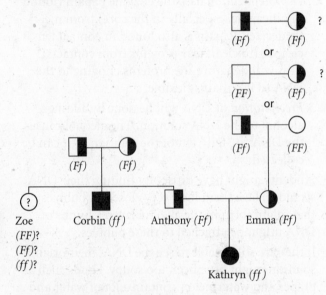

Analyze and Conclude

1. Anthony's parents are both heterozygous *(Ff)*. You cannot tell for sure what the genotypes of Emma's parents are, but at least one is heterozygous and the other could be heterozygous or homozygous for the normal allele *(FF)*.

2. Since both parents are heterozygous, there is a 25 percent chance that Zoë has cystic fibrosis.

3. Anthony and Emma are both heterozygous, so there is a 25 percent chance that they will have another child with cystic fibrosis.

4. Genetic counselors cannot usually draw firm conclusions with just one or two generations; more than one pattern might explain the facts when the information is limited.

5. Cystic fibrosis does not appear to be sex-linked since males and females in this family have the disease.

6. There is always the possibility that family histories can be wrong or incomplete when solving a problem like this one.

Inquiry Extensions

1. Sickle cell disease is a non-sex-linked genetic disorder that affects the shape of the red blood cells. About one in 12 African-Americans has the trait. The trait is also found in populations native to West Africa south of the Sahara, India, Saudi Arabia, Turkey, Greece, Italy, Cuba, and Central and South America. Other ethnic groups that show prevalence for inherited diseases are Ashkenazi Jews and French Canadians (Tay-Sachs disease), and Italians, Greeks, and populations of the Eastern Mediterranean (thalassemia).

2. Accept all reasonable answers. In addition to the European royal families, there is the case of the first European immigrants to America with the traits for hemophilia. A fictional pedigree for a family with a sex-linked (x-linked recessive) trait should resemble the chart below:

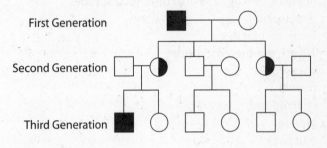

Lab 14 • Classic
What is DNA?

Objectives

- Extract DNA from organic sources.
- Compare the amount of DNA yielded from different sources.
- Design experiments to compare different extraction protocols.

Process Skills

perform procedures, gather and record data, compare and contrast, draw conclusions

Time Allotment

90 minutes the first day
10 minutes to record observations the next day

Materials

various sources of DNA including onions, lima beans, strawberries, non-roasted wheat germ, calf thymus gland, dog testes (from the vet) fresh liver, bacterial cultures, or yeast

various types of alcohol including isopropanol, pure ethyl alcohol, 151-proof liquor (75.5% alcohol). If you choose this option, be sure to conceal its identity.

various detergents including 10% sodium dodecyl sulfate [See Preparation of Solutions, pp. T13–T15], different brands of dish detergent or shampoo without conditioner or other additives, or powdered soaps

various sources of enzymes including meat tenderizer, pineapple juice, contact lens solution, fresh papaya, or crushed papaya tablets

non-iodized salt

hot water bath

ice bath

beakers, 50-mL, 250-mL or large test tubes

paper plate

knife and fork

10-mL graduated cylinder

cheesecloth

funnel

stirring rod

blender

balance

filter paper

wire inoculating loop

thermometer

Alternative Materials

- Glass rods will also work to extract the DNA strands from the mixture.
- A hot plate and aluminum pan will work for the hot water bath. A coffee maker is a quick source of hot water as well.

Preparation

- Have the students measure out 10 mL of alcohol in advance from a flask stored in the freezer. They can leave their graduated cylinders in the freezer until they need them.

Teaching the Lab

- A common problem during the procedure is that the students often pour the alcohol too quickly. Rather than forming two distinct layers, this causes the two to mix. Once that happens, there's not much that can be done.
- Help students understand the terms for the three main steps of the procedure.
  1. *Homogenization* involves blending and heating the strawberry tissue to break down the cell walls. The heat treatment softens the phospholipid bilayers and denatures the DNA bases (which cut DNA). Detergent in the solution further disrupts the cell walls and membranes, releasing the DNA.
  2. *Deproteinization* uses the enzyme papain (found in pineapple, especially in the core) from meat tenderizer. Papain is also found in contact lens cleaner (to clean tear proteins from contacts). This will denature the proteins clinging to the DNA so it remains flexible.
  3. *Precipitation* of DNA will be done by adding alcohol to the DNA solution. The alcohol causes the DNA to "fall" out of the solution so it can be collected.
- Students might have difficulty finding their DNA strands. Have them look very closely at bubbles that might form in the alcohol layer. Clumps of DNA might be attached to these bubbles.
- If they are still unable to see the DNA, their original solution might have been too soupy. Foods such as grapes and watermelon contain a lot of water and therefore the DNA is diluted. Remind students that the DNA extraction should be opaque.

Data and Observations

1. Answers will vary. Possible questions might include: Is there more DNA in kiwi or calf thymus? Is heat really needed for the protocol? Does 99% alcohol work better than 75% alcohol? Will the procedure work as well with out blending?

2. Answers will vary, but the hypothesis should conform to the answer to question 1. For instance, there is more DNA in a plant rather than an animal source.

Sample data for Table 1

DNA data				
Source of DNA or Change in Protocol		Mass of Filter Paper	Mass of DNA + Filter Paper	Mass of DNA
Independent variable	Calf thymus	0.75 g	0.76 g	0.01 g
Control	Kiwi	0.75 g	0.77 g	0.02 g

Analyze and Conclude

1. Because the molecules string together.
2. If the procedure was done correctly, it will come out in strands. DNA is a huge molecule made of many smaller monomers strung together.
3. (2 m x 60 trillion) divided by 380,000 km = 315,789 times
4. Proteins can be structural (e.g., forming hair, skin, or tissues); or proteins can be functional like enzymes.
5. Detergents, like lipids, have hydrophobic and hydrophilic ends that form spheres in water. When you mix detergents and fats in water, the spheres are formed out of both types of molecules, effectively pulling the fat away from water or water solutions. In this case, the detergent helped break up the lipids binding the cell membranes, allowing access to the intracellular material.
6. The investigator would have to use the PCR (polymerase chain reaction) to magnify the amount of DNA and maintain the original sample.
7. Answers will vary. Students might find that their solutions are too watery or that they did not wait long enough for the DNA to move into the alcohol layer.

Inquiry Extensions

1. Do other sources give different amounts of DNA? Do certain properties make it possible to extract more DNA from certain substances? Design an experiment to test these ideas.
2. Does the type of detergent used make a difference in the success of extracting DNA? Do powdered soaps work as well as liquid? Design an experiment to test your hypotheses.

Lab 15 • Classic
Who did it?

Objectives
- Use models to represent DNA fingerprints.
- Infer why DNA patterns differ between individuals.
- Draw conclusions about which suspect was present at a crime scene.

Process Skills
draw conclusions, interpret diagrams

Time Allotment
45 minutes

Materials
mock DNA fingerprint set
magnifying lens
ruler
Figure 1

Preparation
- Obtain bar codes (or photocopies thereof) from various products to prepare mock DNA fingerprint sets. Cut each bar code in half or in thirds, reserving one matching segment from each set to be the criminal's DNA. (Key the criminal's DNA bar code to a number or a symbol on the envelope so that later you can confirm the student's conclusions.) Put six to eight in an envelope, one set for each student or lab group. Then pass out index cards with the criminal's bar code attached for the students to match.
- Have the correct answers to each exercise ready to share with students. Place them on an index card so students can check their work without exposing the answer to the other students.

Teaching the Lab
- Remind students that this is a fictional case. Real crimes are not usually solved as quickly or as easily.
- Circulate around the room to assist students who are having difficulty interpreting the DNA fingerprints.

Data and Observations
Sample data table

DNA Data			
	Bank 1	Bank 2	Bank 3
Suspect A	no	×	no
Suspect B	no	no	×
Suspect C	no	no	no

Analyze and Conclude

1. No, each crime was committed by a different person. You can tell this because none of the DNA strands recovered from the crime scenes matched.

2. There are definite suspects in two of the bank robberies. Bank 2 was robbed by Suspect A. Bank 3 was robbed by Suspect B. Suspect C could be the bank employee, but the police cannot pin this person to any crime. If they have reason to believe that Suspect C was involved, they should keep in mind that he or she might be a bank employee.

3. If Suspect A has an identical twin, the police cannot positively determine that Suspect A robbed Bank 2. Because the twin and the suspect have identical DNA, the police should locate the twin and find out where he or she was during the crime.

4. There is always the possibility of cross contamination during the collection of DNA. Also, the DNA is not a 100 percent positive match in either case. Police need to weigh the odds when deciphering DNA strands.

5. The UPC symbols were a good practice run. They tend to be neater and easier to read than real DNA strands, but the skills of matching up small lines are the same.

6. Every person's DNA fingerprint is unique. The DNA fingerprint is a unique banding fragment produced by restriction fragments. They are unique to each person, unless the person has an identical twin.

Inquiry Extensions

1. Answers will vary. Answers might include questions about how police produced the DNA sample from the crime scene. A defense lawyer might also question how a DNA sample was taken from his or her client. A defense lawyer should also look at the DNA strands and try to convince a jury that there is not enough of a positive match between the strands to show that the evidence at the crime scene was left by his or her client.

2. Answers will vary. Students might report on cases where suspects were convicted because of DNA evidence or prisoners were exonerated because of it. *Be aware that cases of sexual assault could turn up in the course of the students' research.*

Lab 16 • Classic
How do species compare?

Objectives
- Examine a table of amino acid data.
- Interpret the table and find relationships.
- Draw conclusions about how closely related species are.

Process Skills
interpret data, compare and contrast, draw conclusions

Time Allotment
45 minutes

Material
copy of amino acid table

Preparation
- Make sure students know how to read the table before they begin their comparison.
- You may want to review the section on protein synthesis before beginning.

Teaching the Lab
- Ask students to identify the purpose of the lab before they begin.
- The mitochondria of all cells use one small protein, cytochrome c, as part of the energy generation process.
- Remind students that all proteins are made of amino acid sequences that are lined up in specific order.
- Instruct students that each letter in the chart represents one of the 20 amino acids generated by living organisms. Each amino acid is assigned a three-letter code, a shortened version of its chemical name (e.g., alanine: ala; cysteine: cys; etc.). Each three-letter code also has a corresponding single-letter code (e.g., ala: A; cys: C). This system was created because early computer databases could not handle the bulk of three-letter codes. For ease of comparison in the table provided to the students, the letters "J" and "O" were used, when, in fact, those letters are not accepted codes for amino acids.

Teacher Guide and Answers, continued

Data and Observations

Sample answer

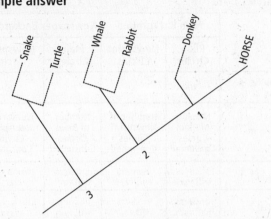

Animal	Number of Amino Acid Positions Different from Horse
Whale	2
Turtle	3
Rabbit	2
Donkey	1
Snake	3

Analyze and Conclude

1. Donkeys are closest, followed by rabbits and whales.
2. Snakes and turtles.
3. Donkeys are most similar to the horse in terms of physical characteristics, as well as in this particular amino acid sequence, while the sequences for the other mammals in the table are more similar to that of the horse than those of the reptiles.
4. No, the table does not provide a basis for comparing species to one another, only to the horse.
5. Answers will vary, but students might recognize that they have examined only part of one amino acid sequence, and that if they looked at more amino acid sequences, they would be able to make a better conclusion.
6. Answers will vary. Students might conclude that the amino acid sequence is not enough to determine the relationships between all species, and that longer sequences or more sequences might be needed to draw firm conclusions.
7. Answers will vary. Students should be careful to check their comparison of the species shown in **Table 1**, and might want to verify the accuracy of the original data in **Table 1**.

Inquiry Extensions

1. Answers will vary. Students should complete charts similar to **Table 2** for each of the species in **Table 1**. Their comparisons should show less variance between species than they might have predicted—most comparisons will show a sequence difference in only one or two positions. Students should perceive that more data, particularly additional parts of the sequence, would be needed to help draw accurate conclusions about how closely related the species are.
2. Answers will vary. Students might find that the sequences available for study show results similar to those in the lab: Animals that share characteristics—or phyla—will differ less in their amino acid sequences.

Lab 17 • Classic
Could you beat natural selection?

Objectives
- Locate organisms (represented by chips) in the natural environment of the classroom.
- Make predictions about survivability of two sets of organisms.
- Simulate predator/prey relationships.
- Complete data tables.
- Graph results.

Process Skills
predict, conclude, model

Time Allotment
45 minutes

Materials

clear chips (25)
red chips (25)
yellow chips (25)
blue chips (25)
graph paper
colored pencils
calculator
one page of newspaper
  apartment rentals
  or stock quotes

sheet of plain paper,
  the same size as
  the newspaper
envelope of circles
  representing prey
forceps or pencil
  with eraser
stopwatch or watch
  with second hand
calculator

Alternative Materials

- Poker chips will work well in Part A, but any colored plastic chips will work.
- Large sheets of butcher paper will work for Part B.

Preparation

- Before class, hide the plastic chips around the classroom. Place some where they will be easily found, and place others in strategic places where they are not so noticeable. You may want to use tape to secure some of the chips in different locations.
- Before starting Part B of the laboratory, prepare an envelope of circle prey for each group. Use scissors or a hole punch to make 30 circles of each type of paper (butcher paper and newspaper).

Teaching the Lab

- Inform the students that the chips in Part A might be difficult to see and that they need to take note of where they find each one.
- For Part B of the lab, dim the lights in the room. This will simulate the environment and time of day in which the organisms are hunted.

Data and Observations

Table 1

Chips Data					
Chip	Original Number	Number Found By Me	Total Number Found	Number Left	Percentage of Chips Left
Clear	25	answers will vary	should be the lowest figure	should be the highest figure	should be the highest figure
Red	25	answers will vary			
Yellow	25	answers will vary			
Blue	25	answers will vary			

Prediction for Part B: Circles that are on a matching background will be less likely to be consumed by a predator.

Table 2

Circles Data				
	Plain Background		Newspaper Background	
	Plain Circles	Newsprint Circles	Plain Circles	Newsprint Circles
Total Population	30	30	30	30
	Number of Plain Circles Consumed	Number of Newsprint Circles Consumed	Number of Plain Circles Consumed	Number of Newsprint Circles Consumed
Trial 1	answers will vary	answers will vary	answers will vary	answers will vary
Trial 2	answers will vary	answers will vary	answers will vary	answers will vary
Trial 3	answers will vary	answers will vary	answers will vary	answers will vary
Team average	answers will vary	answers will vary	answers will vary	answers will vary
Percentage of circles that died	should be lower than X	X	should be higher than Y	Y
Percentage of circles that survived	should be higher than A	A	should be lower than B	B

Analyze and Conclude

1. Answers will vary, but should be one of the opaque, colored chips, not the clear ones. The colored chips will stand out against different backgrounds, while the clear chips will be harder to find.
2. Students should recognize that the clear chips were most difficult to find because they blend in with the surrounding environments.
3. The surroundings on which the chips were placed.
4. Bright colors made these organisms more likely to be picked. In addition, the greater the contrast between the organism's color and the background on which it was placed, the more likely it was to be found.
5. The phenotypes, or outward appearance, of the organisms will be an advantage only if the organism is in the matching environment.
6. Answers will vary, but students might say that the timing, inaccurate counting by the predator, or dropped prey were sources of error.
7. The more an organism blends in with its environment, the more likely it is to survive predation. This was demonstrated in Part A of the lab as well.

Inquiry Extensions

1. Topics will vary, but accept any well-researched effort. There are many examples of insects whose coloration or body types resemble sticks or leaves in their habitats. Higher-level students may also discuss the use of Batesian or Mullerian mimicry to avoid predation, or aggressive mimicry to attract prey or deceive predators (angler fish, viruses).

2. Answers will vary, but students may identify characteristics such as streamlined body shape in sharks or dolphins for speed and long, narrow tongues of hummingbirds and anteaters for access to preferred foods. For the second part of the question, accept any well-reasoned premise. For example, because of increasing levels of ozone in the lower atmosphere, organisms that can tolerate or use ozone could be selected for. In humans, resistance to adding fat cells during long periods of physical inactivity might be selected for in increasingly high-tech environments.

Lab 18 • Design Your Own

Does this animal walk on four legs or two?

Objectives

- Devise a plan to compare the limbs and pelvis of a gorilla, australopithecine, and a present-day human.
- Make predictions about the differences between structures of bipedal and quadrupedal animals.
- Extrapolate the information gathered to a discussion on natural selection.
- Determine whether the australopithecines were habitual upright walkers (bipeds).

Process Skills

pose questions, make predictions, use models, make inferences

Time Allotment

45 minutes

Materials

calculator
human skeleton
diagram of pelvises and femurs of chimpanzee, australopithecine, and human. [See How to Use the Student Models, pp. T24–T31.]
diagrams of gorilla, australopithecine, and human [See How to Use the Student Models, pp. T24–T31.]
scale drawing of human and gorilla cut out and mounted on card stock
glue
scissors
ruler

Possible Hypotheses

A. If the center of gravity is in front of the pelvis, the organism will need to use its front limbs to support its weight when moving.

B. If the center of gravity is in front of the pelvis, the arms will need to be longer.

C. If the weight is evenly distributed above and below the pelvis, the organism will be able to walk upright.

D. If the vertical lines of force are drawn from the hip down, the wear pattern will be on the outside of the femur in an upright walker.

Possible Procedure

1. Measure the length of the arms and legs of the human, australopithecine, and gorilla on the diagram. Record this information in the data table.

2. Cut out the figures of the human and chimpanzee. Use the pencil end of an eraser to find the centers of gravity (point of balance) for each figure. Record your findings.

3. Look at other students in the room. Do humans usually keep their legs straight or bent? Record your observations.

4. Again notice the stance of your classmates. Is the position of the lumbar region (lower back) in humans normally straight or curved? Record this in your data table.

5. Use the same diagrams for the gorilla and the australopithecine that you used before to notice the normal position of their legs and lumbar regions. Record these observations in your table.

6. Obtain a diagram of the pelvis and femurs of a chimpanzee, australopithecine, and a human.

Draw a vertical line from the star to the bottom of the figure. This is the weight-bearing axis. Record the location of this axis in your data table.

Preparation

- Make photocopies of the human and gorilla outlines on card stock. These can be used for center-of-gravity determination.
- You can include a scale diagram of the human skeleton if students do not want to measure the lengths on their own bodies.
- If possible, borrow a human skeleton from the anatomy lab for students to measure and observe.

Teaching the Lab

- Make sure students understand where the lumbar region and pelvis are located.
- Provide pictures of the animals so students can have a frame of reference as they make their observations and measurements.
- Be sure that students understand that scientists are still debating the reasons why humans became bipedal. Students should also consider which came first— bipedalism or the expansion of the brain. Was it necessary for humans to become bipedal first for the brain to expand or vice versa? (Answer: Bipedalism came first.) Since that time, we have had two major brain expansions.

Data and Observations

Sample data table

Comparison of Bipedal and Quadrupedal Anthropoids			
	Gorilla	Australopithecine	Human
Arm length	approximately 55 mm	approximately 45 mm	approximately 40 mm
Leg length	approximately 45 mm	approximately 53 mm	approximately 60 mm
Position of leg	bent at knees	slightly less bent at knees	straight
Shape of lumbar region	straight	curved	curved
Center of gravity	in front of pelvis	center of pelvis	center of pelvis
Weight-bearing axis	inside edge of femur	outside edge of femur	outside edge of femur

Analyze and Conclude

1. The gorilla probably has the tendency to fall forward since its center of gravity is in front of its pelvis. A gorilla uses its long arms to compensate for this tendency.
2. Most of the body weight in a gorilla is in the upper body. The body weight of a human tends to be concentrated near the waist and middle of the body.
3. Australopithecines probably walked on two legs. The center of gravity of this animal was more similar to the center of gravity of a modern human. The weight was distributed above and below the pelvis equally.
4. Bipedalism allowed the animals to walk upright. This made obtaining food and watching for predators easier. It also allowed the animals to manipulate things with their hands more effectively.
5. Answers will vary, but students might have had difficulty measuring the bones on the diagram. They might think it was difficult to compare the three animals, or they might have had difficulty finding the center of gravity for each animal.
6. Answers will vary, but most student groups should have found similar trends.

Write and Discuss

Students whose hypothesis stated that an organism that has its weight evenly distributed above and below the pelvis would be able to walk upright would have found support for the hypothesis in this investigation.

Inquiry Extensions

1. Students should report that the two primary hypotheses scientists consider for why humans are bipedal focus on food gathering from trees and nurturing of young. Research on chimpanzee ecology and australopithecine functional morphology (study of how muscles would have attached to the bones) suggests that both organisms tend toward bipedalism when reaching for fruit in low-hanging tree branches.

Another hypothesis focuses on the reproductive imperative and early forms of pair bonding. In brief, males who were more efficient at food gathering—those who walked upright and could carry food in their arms—were more adept at bringing that food to females who were relatively limited in their foraging range by the needs of nursing infants. The provided food would presumably also go to the child at an earlier age, allowing it to stop nursing. This, in turn, would allow the female to resume ovulation, and the male would have a greater chance at producing more offspring and passing his genes to a new generation.

2. Human ancestry is very complex. Encourage students to create a branching family tree so they can trace direct as well as distant ancestors.

Lab 19 • Classic
What is a taxonomic key?

Objectives
- Use a key to identify common denominations of money.
- Examine the method used to make a key.
- Construct a key to identify a group of organisms.

Time Allotment
45 minutes

Process Skills
identify, construct, model, compare and contrast

Materials
set of coins (penny, nickel, dime, quarter*) and bills ($1 and $5)
pen or pencil
reference material
animal envelope
index cards

* *To match the designations in the key, avoid using quarters from the States series.*

Alternative Materials
- set of play money, or real coins and photocopies of bills

Preparation
Photocopy the black-line masters for Lab 19. [See How to Use the Student Models, pp. T24-T31.] Cut out individual animals (or have students cut them out). The animals are:

a. giraffe   g. dik dik
b. camel   h. pig
c. llama   i. hippopotamus
d. African buffalo j. mountain goat
e. bushbuck   k. sheep
f. pronghorn antelope

  In addition, if color images can be made available, they might also aid in the classification key exercise.

Teaching the Lab
- Students might find it useful to tape the animal picture on the index card where they write the characteristic.
- Emphasize to students that not everyone's key will be identical. There are different characteristics that they might choose to highlight.
- Students should work in pairs for this activity. Be sure to pair stronger students with those who might need a little more help.

Data and Observations
1. Taxonomic Key for Money
1A.	Metal	Go to statement 2
1B.	Paper	Go to statement 5
2A.	Brown (copper)	penny
2B.	Silver	Go to statement 3
3A.	Smooth edge	nickel
3B.	Ridges around the edge	Go to statement 4
4A.	Torch on back	dime
4B.	Eagle on back	quarter
5A.	Number 1 in the corners	$1 bill
5B.	Number 5 in the corners	$5 bill

2. Sample Taxonomic Key for Order Artiodactyla
1A.	Long neck	giraffe
1B.	Not a long neck	Go to statement 2
2A.	Horns or antlers	Go to statement 3
2B.	No horns or antlers	Go to statement 7
3A.	Horns or antlers point up	Go to statement 4
3B.	Horns or antlers point down	African buffalo
4A.	Horns or antlers twisted	bushbuck
4B.	Horns or antlers straight	Go to statement 5
5A.	Horns or antlers curve in	Go to statement 6
5B.	Horns or antlers curve back	mountain goat
6A.	Small animal	dik dik
6B.	Large animal	pronghorn antelope
7A.	Lives on land	Go to statement 8
7B.	Lives in water	hippopotamus
8A.	Long legs	Go to statement 9
8B.	Short legs	Go to statement 10
9A.	Has humps on back	camel
9B.	Has no humps on back	llama
10A.	Has thick coat of wool	sheep
10B.	No wool	pig

Analyze and Conclude

1. A classification key is a set of steps and character-istics that can be used to identify an organism.
2. Answers will vary. Students might comment on the neck length, size, absence or presence of horns, and the way in which the horns point on the animal's head. These are the most obvious observable characteristics.
3. Bushbucks have twisted horns while antelope have curved horns.
4. Mountain goats have horns, and sheep do not.
5. Answers will vary. Each team should review another team's work for internal logic and consistency. Students should point out the characteristics that the classmates focused on to initiate the key.
6. Answers will vary. Students might find that their approximation of size of the animals is not correct.

Inquiry Extensions

1. Provide research materials to help students with this exercise. Students might choose to focus on characteristics other than physical features; they might select habitats, food source, or means of locomotion as the traits in the key.
2. Accept all reasonable posters. The best posters will
   - show relationships between the most similar items;
   - use detailed graphics;
   - demonstrate additional research.

Lab 20 • Design Your Own
Can you filter out cholera?

Objectives

- Form a hypothesis about what type of filter would be the best to filter water containing copepods.
- Design a filter.
- Compare the number of copepods in a water sample before filtering to the number of copepods after filtering.

Process Skills

model, form a hypothesis, compare and contrast, collect and analyze data

Time Allotment

45 minutes

Materials

simulated river-water sample
funnel
clean droppers (2)
large beaker
small beaker
graduated cylinder

microscope
slides with cell counter or slides with grids
cover slips
metric ruler
squares of cloth

Alternative Materials

- Use silk, cotton, nylon (pantyhose), or polyester for the sari cloth. Also, make cheesecloth available.

Possible Hypothesis

A filter made of silk cloth will provide the most effective means of removing copepods from water.

Possible Procedure

1. Put on personal safety equipment before starting the experiment.
2. Obtain a water sample from the teacher.
3. Take a small dropperful of water, and create a wet mount slide.
4. Observe the water under the microscope, and count the number of copepods.
5. Move the slide, and count again. Do a count in each corner of the slide.
6. Get a funnel, a beaker, and the silk cloth. Fold the cloth five times so that you have a tight square.
7. Place the square of fabric in the funnel.
8. Pour 50 mL of river water into the filter that has been placed in the funnel.
9. After the water has drained out, take a clean dropperful of the filtered water.
10. Observe that sample under the microscope, and count the number of copepods in each corner of the slide, as was done before.
11. Clean up, and wash hands with soap and water.
12. Complete the data table and questions in this lab.

Preparation

- Provide pond water that has a known population of copepods, or order a sample from a biological supply store.
- Cut cloth into 15 cm × 15 cm squares before class starts.

Teaching the Lab

- Make sure that students are passing the water through all the folds in the cloth. Running the water along the edges of the cloth will not filter it.
- Students might want to examine the cloth after it has been used as a filter to see the copepods that were trapped.
- Make sure that students keep the volume of water being filtered consistent.
- Ask students to discuss what differences in materials might make one type of cloth a better filter than another.

Data and Observations

Sample data table

Number of Copepods		
	Before Filtration	After Filtration
2 mL sample	18	2

Analyze and Conclude

1. Answers will vary, but students should discuss how they fit the filter into the funnel while making it thick enough for the water to pass through several times.
2. Answers will vary. Some students might find that their filter removes up to 50 percent of the copepods.
3. Students might notice that sediment or plant material was also caught in the filter.
4. The control was the water that was not filtered. The number of copepods remained the same in this unfiltered sample.
5. Answers will vary and might include a miscount of the number of copepods before or after filtering, or damage to the filter itself.
6. Answers will vary. Students who used more tightly woven fabrics such as silk or nylon would have more success than those who used cheesecloth.

Write and Discuss

Answers will vary. Students should include the number of copepods before and after filtering and analysis of the performance of materials if more than one type of cloth was tested.

Inquiry Extensions

1. Designs will vary. Students might use things such as paper towels or coffee filters. Accept all reasonable designs. Students should demonstrate an understanding that even without obvious signs of contamination, the sample might not be safe to drink.
2. Accept all well-planned and well-presented campaigns. A sample campaign might include distribution of free T-shirts with instructions on how to turn the shirt into a filter.

Lab 21 • Design Your Own
Do protists have good table manners?

Objectives

- Form a hypothesis about how environmental factors impact the eating habits of paramecia.
- Observe paramecia eating under a microscope.
- Identify a variable to test.
- Introduce an environmental variable, and record any changes in the paramecia's eating habits.

Process Skills

form hypotheses, compare and contrast, control variables

Time Allotment

45 minutes

Materials

microscope	ice
slides and cover slips	latex or plastic gloves
eye droppers (2)	warm water
sample of pond water	(26°C to 30°C)
yeast mixture	cold water
data table	(14°C to 18°C)
table lamp	caffeine solution (1 g/L)
methyl cellulose or	sugar
3% gelatin solution	

Alternative Materials

Paramecia can be purchased from a biology supply store to ensure an adequate supply of the organism.

Possible Hypothesis

Paramecia will eat faster in a warm environment than they will in a cold environment.

Possible Procedure

1. Examine your sample of pond water to check if there are enough paramecia to study. If not, obtain a different sample from your teacher. Make two sets of slides; one will act as a control.

2. Fill a small beaker with warm water and one with ice water. Place a dropper in each of them.

3. When you have spotted several paramecia under the microscope, add a small drop of the yeast mixture to the slide just beside the slide cover. Once you observe the paramecia eating, add a small drop of room-temperature water near them. Observe how they eat. Take special note of the speed with which they eat and if their method changes.

4. Repeat step 3 using a new sample of pond water with visible paramecia. Again, drop food near them, and observe their eating habits. This time, add a drop of cold water, and note any change.

5. Repeat these steps a few times to make sure you are observing the effects of the warm and cold water.

Preparation

- Gather pond water samples in advance.
- Mix one envelope of prepared yeast with 500 mL of lukewarm water to provide food for the paramecia.
- Prepare caffeine solution by mixing caffeine powder in distilled water.

Teaching the Lab

- Circulate throughout the room to help students with their microscope skills.
- If the paramecia are moving too quickly for the students to observe, use a methyl cellulose or 3-percent gelatin solution to slow the protists.
- Provide several textbooks or other reference materials that have illustrations of paramecia so students can be sure they are observing the right organism.
- Review the student procedures to ensure they make sense and will be effective.

Data and Observations

1. Answers will vary. Student drawings should show at least one paramecium with cilia moving food toward a vacuole, and/or a paramecium surrounding its food and engulfing it.

2. Students might report on the movement of cilia, cilia sweeping bits of the yeast mixture toward the vacuoles, or the opening or closing of vacuoles.

3. Answers will vary. Sample answer: The paramecia slowed down when the temperature of the environment decreased.

Analyze and Conclude

1. Paramecia eat by engulfing food.

2. Cilia draw the food source toward the paramecia.

3. Answers will vary depending on the second variable tested. Students who tested cold and warm water should have used a second slide as a control.

4. Answers will vary. Students might find that the factor they chose to examine had no impact on the eating habits.

5. Answers will vary depending on the formulation of the hypothesis. In the sample case used here, the hypothesis was correct.

6. Answers will vary. Students might find that keeping track of the paramecia was a problem. Or they might have had difficulty determining if their environmental factor really changed the behavior.

7. Answers will vary based on the class experiences. Students who changed the light conditions should have recorded that the paramecia gravitated toward the lighted side more than the dark side. Students who added caffeine to the slide should have recorded an increase in the rate of movement. Students who added a sugar solution to the water should have recorded an increase in the rate of movement. Students who increased the available food supply should have recorded more eating.

Write and Discuss

Answers will vary. Students might say that their hypothesis was not supported because they based their assumptions on their own experiences (e.g., preferring to eat more in cold weather and less in hot weather.)

Inquiry Extensions

1. Answers will vary. Students might need reference materials in order to identify the organisms they saw in the pond water. Examples of other protists typically found in pond water include the protozoans amoeba, didinium, and euglena, and algae such as spirulina, polycystis, closterium, and frustulla. The protozoans' eating method is largely defined by their shape. Ciliates eat in a fashion similar to a paramecia. Amoebates surround

their food and engulf it. Flagellates use whip like projections to swim after food.

2. Answers will vary. Paramecia also ingest bacteria and algae. Suitable varieties can be cultured or obtained for student experiments. Eating habits of paramecia do not substantially change with the food source.

Lab 22 • Classic
What are mushroom spores?

Objectives
- Identify the parts of a variety of supermarket mushrooms.
- Learn about the spores of a mushroom by creating and examining a spore print.
- Determine how spores are spread by making a model from a balloon and cotton balls.

Process Skills
observe, investigate, model

Time Allotment
One 45-minute lab. Part B will require 10 minutes, two days after it has started. The students will not be able to complete all of the questions until the spore print has been made.

Materials
magnifying lens	large plastic container
mushrooms of different	with lid
varieties bought from	round balloon
local grocery store	cotton balls
dissecting probe	tape
paper towels	ruler or stiff stick
white paper	modeling clay
pin	

Alternative Materials
- prepared microscope slide of mushroom gills and/or mixed spores
- microscope
- Stereomicroscope (if available)
- Confetti can be used instead of cotton ball fragments.

Preparation
- Get a variety of mushrooms from the local grocery store. Include common mushrooms that students might be familiar with as well as more exotic mushrooms to add variety to the exercise. They should have stalks as well as caps.
- Sometimes the mushrooms are not open enough to use. Purchase some several days in advance to give them time to open.
- If students will not have time to revisit part two of the lab for several days, you may want to prepare the spore prints in advance.

Teaching the Lab
- Encourage groups to compare and contrast the fruiting bodies of different types of mushrooms.
- The color of spores is a characteristic used to identify mushrooms. The use of white paper (and a binocular scope, if available) will help ensure accurate observations. Ask students to sketch the spores and their fruiting bodies.
- Remind students not to eat any of the mushrooms you have given them in this lab, or any that they find in the wild.

Data and Observations
1.

gills
stipe (stem)
cap

2.

3.
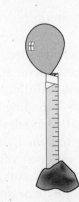

The pieces of the cotton ball dispersed in a rough circle approximately 1.2 m in diameter.

Copyright © Glencoe/McGraw-Hill, a division of The McGraw-Hill Companies, Inc.

Analyze and Conclude

1. These structures are hyphae. They are the fungal cells. All mushrooms have them. The student's ability to remove them from the stalk in each sample will depend on the types of mushroom.

2. The hyphae hold the mushrooms in place and help them absorb food or water. Above-level learners may note that fungi secrete enzymes from the hyphae then absorb the digested nutrients. One of the things that distinguishes fungi from other heterotrophs is that they are absorptive.

3. Answers will vary. Students might be able to estimate how many spores are on each radiating line and then multiply by the number of lines in their print. Students should recognize that mushrooms usually grow in moist, warm, and dark places. Spores that do not immediately germinate will remain dormant until the proper growth conditions are met, or they will die.

4. Just as the air in the balloon scattered the cotton balls far away from the balloon, air currents can carry spores far from the mushrooms. Because so many spores are produced, the chances that the spores will land in a favorable environment are great.

5. Answers will vary. Some students might mention that they find a visual display easier to understand.

6. Answers will vary. Students might have found it difficult to identify the parts of a mushroom, or to count the spores; or their balloon might not have spread the cotton balls.

7. The wind would make the model more realistic, spreading the spores even farther from the source. This would also affect the pattern of dispersal.

Inquiry Extensions

1. Common poisonous mushrooms include the fly argaic and the death cap.

2. Answers will vary. Students who research this topic will discover general methods for active spore release: the bursting cell, ballistospore discharge, and the catapult or "rounding off." Students might recognize that, after release, spores can be transported by mammals, birds, insects, leaves, and water. Above-level learners might discover that some spores can survive passage through an animal's gut, to be dispersed in dung.

Lab 23 • Classic

How do ferns, mosses, and conifers reproduce?

Objectives

- Examine samples of ferns, mosses, and conifers.
- Compare characteristics of seeds, spores, and pollen in each.
- Infer how these characteristics have made survival of each plant possible.

Process Skills

analyze, examine, compare and contrast, infer

Time Allotment

45–60 minutes (45 minutes for lab, an additional 15 minutes for discussion)

Materials

fern fronds (with sori)   forceps
moss sample (with   paper towels
    sporophytes)   dropper
pine cones (male and   water
    female)   petri dish
diagrams of the   magnifying lens or
    life cycles of   stereomicroscope,
    ferns, mosses, and   if available
    conifers   colored pencils
scalpel

Preparation

- Some students might be allergic to pollen. Advise those students to take proper precautions (e.g., face masks) before starting the lab.

- Distribute diagrams of the life cycles of mosses, ferns, and conifers from How to Use the Student Models, pp. T24–T31, or some other source. If possible, use color photocopies, posters, colored prints, or artwork.

- If possible, have students examine live plants instead of samples. Going outside to see real examples is preferable.

Teaching the Lab

• Ask students to think about what they know about ferns, mosses, and conifers and the environment they grow in before starting the lab. This will help students focus their attention on the differences between these plants.

• Circulate around the room to head off any problems or answer any questions that arise.

Data and Observations

1. Accept all reasonable diagrams. For the fern, students should draw the underside of the pinna and show the attached sporangia. If moss are in the fruiting stage, students should note the fruiting structure, including the filament, and the sporangium. Male and female pine cones might be attached to the same branch and found in clusters. Generally speaking, the male cones are soft and fleshy, while the female cones are the "classic" hard-finned cone (depending on the stage at which it was harvested).

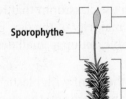

Female pine cone

Male pine cone

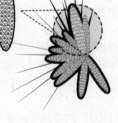

Sporophythe — { Sporangium

Filament (or stalk)

Gametophyte

Moss fruiting body

2. Accept all reasonable diagrams. Drawings of the fern spore should show sorus, and if possible, the spores within. Student drawings of the microscopic view of the moss could show the antheridial head, sperm in antheridium, or the ovule in the archegonium. Student drawings of the seeds from a conifer should show the seed body and, depending on the species, any winglike structure used to aid dispersal.

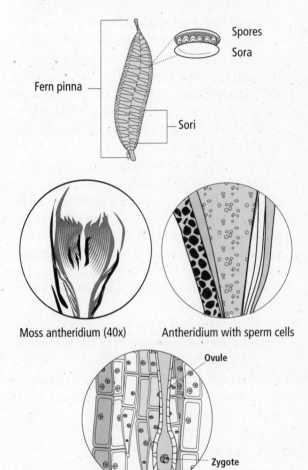

Spores

Sora

Fern pinna

Sori

Moss antheridium (40x)   Antheridium with sperm cells

Ovule

Zygote

Moss archegonium (100x)

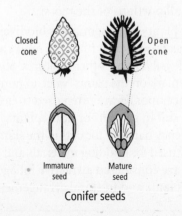

Closed cone   Open cone

Immature seed   Mature seed

Conifer seeds

Analyze and Conclude

1. Students should notice the black spots on the underside of the frond and identify these as spore capsules.

2. Students should notice a lack of seeds in the moss plant. They should see a green, fuzzy plant with tiny rootlike structures called rhizomes.

3. The pine cone might have some leaves, or needles, attached to it. The students might notice the difference between male and female cones. The female cone might have scales with two ovules.

4. The pine tree is a gymnosperm, and it goes through the steps of pollination, fertilization, seed development, and dispersal. The ferns and mosses lack seeds, so they have a different life cycle, which includes the need for water so the sperm can swim to the egg.

5. The fern capsule will develop into a structure with both male and female reproductive structures. The young plant will develop after pollination occurs, whereas the conifer seed is already fertilized. They both contain what is needed for the future generation. The moss sporophyte is similar to the fern capsule in that it contains spores which will be released under the right conditions.

6. Inability to prepare a fine enough section, or lack of discernible structures in the specimens are possible sources of error.

7. Conifers need sandy soil and deep water sources. Ferns and mosses need a moist environment to spread the sperm cells.

Inquiry Extensions

1. Accept all reasonable designs. Students should make note of the mechanisms (osmosis and diffusion) that allow water and nutrients to reach all portions of the moss.

2. These plants are essential for biodiversity. They serve as producers within the food chain and provide habitats for other creatures. Students might also remark on the plants' value to humans—for instance, mosses are often used to hold moisture in the soil in gardens or houseplants, or as an emergency bandage for cuts in the skin. Pines are widely used for building materials and furniture. Ferns are considered attractive foliage for houseplants and in floral arrangements.

Lab 24 • Design Your Own
Do plants sweat?

Objectives

- Form a hypothesis about how transpiration is affected by a change in an environmental condition.
- Design an experiment to test the impact of this environmental condition.

Process Skills

form hypotheses, control variables

Time Allotment

45 minutes to set up
10 minutes per day for several days

Materials

electric fan   small plastic bags
food coloring   (not the zippered kind)
live plant   ties
pipette   petroleum jelly
scissors   water
small beaker

Possible Hypothesis

If plants are exposed to an environment with more direct sunlight, then the rate of transpiration will increase.

Possible Procedure

1. Choose a location in the classroom that receives direct sunlight for a majority of the day. If such a location is not available, set up a small desk lamp to simulate the sun.

2. Cover two leaves of the plant with plastic bags. Gently tie the plastic bags around the stem of the leaf.

3. Ensure that one of the leaves is in the direct sunlight.

4. The other leaf covered by the bag needs to be shaded from the sunlight. Cover this leaf and bag with a small lunch bag.

5. During the next few days, check on the plant. Any water that is leaving the leaf though transpiration will collect in the plastic bags as condensation.

Preparation

- Provide space in various locations around the room for students to store their plants during the experimental time.
- Caution: Remind students to be careful if fans are used. Keep them away from water, and plug them into a GFI-protected circuit.
- Remind students to handle sharp scissors with care. Scissors can cut or pierce the skin.
- Use only fresh plants. Plants placed in water over several days will have bacterial or mold growth.

Teaching the Lab

- Review the student's procedures to make sure that the experimental design will show results.

Data and Observations

Sample data table

Transpiration in Two Leaves			
Day	Water Added to Plant Pot	Leaf in Sun	Leaf in Dark
1	50 mL	small amount of water vapor in the plastic bag	small amount of water vapor in the plastic bag
2	50 mL	0.5 mL water	small amount of water vapor in the plastic bag
3	0 mL	0.5 mL water	0.2 mL water
4	50 mL	0.4 mL water	small amount of water vapor in the plastic bag
5	50 mL	0.6 mL water	0.2 mL water
6	0 mL	0.5 mL water	small amount of water vapor in the plastic bag
7	0 mL	0.3 mL water	small amount of water vapor in the plastic bag
8	50 mL	0.5 mL water	no water vapor
9	50 mL	0.4 mL water	no water vapor
10	50 mL	0.5 mL water	small amount of water vapor in the plastic bag

Analyze and Conclude

1. Answers will vary depending on which factors the students chose. In this example, the student chose exposure to sunlight as the variable. Based on the scenario provided in the introduction, the student wanted to see if plants in shaded areas can retain more water than plants in bright light.
2. Answers will vary. Plants kept in low light and high humidity will have lower transpiration rates than those in bright light and low humidity.
3. Answers will vary. Students might mention humidity, temperature, wind conditions, and seasons as well as other factors. Accept all reasonable answers.
4. Answers will vary depending on student's experimental design. The control of the experiment should involve a plant that is not affected by the variable being tested in order to determine if the change seen was due to the environmental factor itself.
5. Answers will vary. Responses can include lack of control over air movement in the room, poor lighting, and length of time of experiment.
6. Answers will vary. The student who studied sunlight as her variable could exchange data with someone who studied the effects of wind. The data might show that there was more transpiration in the plant in windy conditions.

Write and Discuss

Answers will vary. Students should provide a well thought-out answer that discusses their original hypothesis. Accept responses that show reflection. In this example, the student should point out that his or her hypothesis was supported, and that sunlight caused more transpiration than in the control as measured by the amount of water captured in the plastic bag. A question could be: "Is it more advantageous to the plant to risk losing water to have more sun exposure for photosynthesis?"

Inquiry Extensions

1. Answers will vary. Maps should include the location of other major trees, bodies of water, the location of the Sun at that moment, shadows from buildings, watering systems, and other factors.

2. Answers will vary. Accept all well thought-out designs. Students might elect to determine if a mild acid or base solution can be detected in the water given off in transpiration by using pH paper. Help students select chemicals and amounts that can be absorbed by the plant without immediately killing it.

Lab 25 • Classic
How does a flower grow?

Objectives
- Dissect flowers to examine female and male parts.
- Measure and describe characteristics of flowers.
- Make and label flower diagrams.
- Draw conclusions about reproduction in plants.

Process Skills
observe, infer, measure

Time Allotment
60 minutes

Materials
paper towels	cover slip
dropper	scalpel
magnifying lens	cellophane tape
flower identification	water
book (field guide)	metric ruler
microscope	lens paper
slide	colored pencils
large flowers (2)	

Alternative Materials
- forceps or toothpicks for dissecting flowers

Preparation
- Provide a variety of flowers. Use large to medium sized flowers such as gladiolas, roses, hibiscus, tulips, and lilies. Be sure to give students access to one monocot, such as a gladiola or alastromeria, and one dicot, such as a rose. Grocery stores are good sources for flowers for this lab. Use caution when selecting sources for the flowers—they could have bacteria or mold.
- Check for pollen allergies among students. Provide pictures or prepared slides for students with allergies to examine.

- Remind students to wash their hands with soap and water after handling the flowers.

Teaching the Lab
- Review the use of a microscope and how to make a wet mount.
- Students can usually tap the stamen of the flower to get a sample of pollen. In some recently opened flowers, the stamen might need to be crushed against the microscope slide.
- You might need to help students distinguish between the stamen and pistils.
- Students might need help opening the pistil all the way down to the ovary which might be deep in the sepal area.
- Students might want to save pollen that drops off the flower at the beginning of the lab for Part B.
- Depending on the species, the top of the pistil can display any of a variety of textures: rough, smooth, sticky, branched, or feathered. Answers will vary based on the type of flower.
- The number of chambers in an ovary is equal to or a multiple of the number of petals and stamens.

Data and Observations
Sample data for Table 1

Flower Data			
Part of Flower	Flower 1 (Monocot)	Flower 2 (Dicot)	Description
Petals	6	5	Answers will vary.
Sepals	6	5	Answers will vary.
Stamens	6	5	Answers will vary.
Pistil compartments	6	10	Answers will vary.
Ovules	3	5	Answers will vary.

Analyze and Conclude
1. The sepals reach up from the base of the flower and cover the petals. Sometimes they cover the entire petal, and sometimes they do not.
2. Sample answer: Not all petals were the same on one flower. The outer ones tended to be bigger and heartier, while the inner ones were smaller and seemed more delicate.
3. They were arranged in circles in the following order from outside in: sepals, petals, stamens, and the pistil in the middle.

4. The number of chambers in the ovaries is equal to or a multiple of the number of petals and stamens.

5. The function of these flowers is reproduction. The sepals protect the flower and serve as a sturdy base. The petals attract animals that will act as pollinators. The stamens produce pollen. The pistil holds the egg cells.

6. Answers will vary. Students might mention how the pistil is taller than the stamens so that the flower does not self-pollinate.

7. Answers will vary, but students might mention that they were not precise when cutting the flower with the scalpel, or their use of the microscope might have been deficient.

8. Answers will vary depending on the flowers the students examined. Flower parts of monocots are usually in threes or in multiples of three. Flower parts in dicots are usually in multiples of four or five.

Inquiry Extensions

1. Answers will vary. Students should at least discuss how the flowers are arranged on the plant, how the parts of the flower are arranged, how the flowers are oriented to one another on the plant, the most likely way that these flowers are pollinated, and if the flower is a monocot or a dicot.

2. [If flowers are not readily available when this lab is being taught, provide a variety of fruit, including rose hips, if possible, for students to examine.] Answers will vary. Most fruits purchased in a grocery store will rely on animals for dispersal. Coconuts are an exception.

Lab 26 • Classic
Is that symmetrical?

Objectives
• Identify lines of symmetry in animal samples.
• Model symmetry in the human face.
• Infer relationships between body structure and survival.

Process Skills
infer, model, conclude

Time Allotment
45 minutes

Materials
pencil
ruler
plain, unlined paper
selection of photocopies of full facial portraits cut in half lengthwise
tracing paper
glue or rubber cement
cellophane tape

modeling clay in two colors per team
plastic knife
small mirror

Suggested specimens:
preserved butterfly
preserved fish
preserved sea urchin
preserved sea anenome
preserved star fish

Alternative Materials
• Photographs/diagrams of the animals will work in place of the samples.
• Claylike commercial preparations sold in toy stores can be substituted for the clay.

Preparation
• Have several examples of items showing both types of symmetry to show students before they begin. A bicycle tire, a maple leaf, and an orange are all good examples.
• Assemble a collection of photographs that can be used in place of preserved animals if necessary.
• For Part B, select five or six good portraits in advance and photocopy them so that the images are 10–15 cm tall. If all students are working with black-and-white images, the non-artists might have a little more confidence in their drawing skills.
• Remind students to handle the animal samples with care and to wash their hands after handling the specimens; preservatives can be toxic.

Teaching the Lab
• Circulate through the lab to help students overcome any problems that might arise.
• Set a time limit for students to complete their drawings. Encourage students to complete their drawings in the time available; even students who are not proficient at drawing can be successful at this exercise.

Data and Observations

Table 1

Symmetry Data				
Animal	**Movement**	**Habitat**	**Symmetry**	**Diagram**
Butterfly	flies	open fields, grassy areas	bilateral	
Fish	swims	open water	bilateral	
Sea urchin	slow, crawling motion	tidal pool	radial	
Sea star	slow, crawling motion	tidal pool	radial	
Sea anemone	stationary	ocean floor or reef	radial	

Analyze and Conclude

1. The butterfly, fish, and human face show bilateral symmetry. The sea urchin, sea star, and sea anemone show radial symmetry.

2. Bilaterally symmetrical animals are capable of a greater number and range of movements, and generally, more speed. Radially symmetrical animals are slow movers or stationary.

3. Answers will vary. Students should infer that bilateral symmetry allows for balance and speed, which is good for both predators and prey. Point out to students that some bilateral animals, such as tortoises and sloths, are notoriously slow moving, so bilateral symmetry does not equate with speed. But a bilateral body plan does support directional movement, allowing an organism more options in terms of food, defense, and mating.

4. Most students will probably discuss their inability to draw an accurate tracing of the face.

5. Most students should say no. When lab partners compare their faces, the mirror images should be different from the actual face. No one's face is perfectly symmetrical.

6. Answers will vary. Students might report that a radially symmetrical pattern is simpler to model.

Inquiry Extensions

1. Answers will vary. Students might point out that most vessels (cups, bowls, pans, and vases) are radially symmetrical, allowing them to hold a variety of objects. Ladders, hand tools, and vehicles are bilaterally symmetrical and require balance for effective use.

2. Answers will vary. Most students who live away from the oceans will view pets (including fish and reptiles), agricultural animals, or wildlife, all of which display bilateral symmetry. Only those who can observe ocean animals such as sea urchins, sand dollars, or jellyfish will be able to report on animals with radial symmetry (one exception being the freshwater hydra).

Lab 27 • Design Your Own
Which will the worm choose?

Objectives

- Identify environmental factors that a worm might favor.
- Design a laboratory experiment to determine which condition an earthworm favors.
- Compare the behaviors of two earthworms under a variety of conditions.
- Draw a conclusion about the conditions preferred by these organisms.

Process Skills

develop hypotheses, interpret data, conclude from data

Time Allotment

45 minutes

Materials

stopwatch
water
paper towels
cardboard
soil
sand
non-mercury
 thermometer
earthworms (2)

clean spray bottle
shallow pan
flashlight or desk lamp
 (Use caution: The heat can cause drying which would complicate the variables.)
ruler
dropper

Alternative Materials

- Cake pans, lunch trays, or dissecting pans can be used as shallow pans.
- Sow bugs or hoppers may be used in place of earthworms.

Possible Hypothesis

If earthworms can move to either a dry or a wet surface, they will move to the wet surface.

Possible Procedure

1. Use a dropper or spray bottle to sprinkle water on worms. Be sure to keep the worms moist at all times.
2. Fill the tray with soil. Spray water on one side of the soil, keep the other side dry.
3. Place the earthworms in the middle of the tray, lengthwise across the line dividing the two environments. Be sure that half of each earthworm's body is on the damp soil and half is on the dry soil.
4. Cover the tray with the cardboard. Wait five minutes and then remove the cardboard.
5. Record your observations.
6. Repeat steps 3–5 two more times.

Preparation

- Earthworms can be purchased from a biological supply store or a bait shop. You can also gather them from loose garden soil.
- Remind students to treat the earthworms with care. They should not try to kill or harm the worms in any way.
- Use only GFI-protected circuits for any desk lamps that are used.
- Do not get water near or on any electrical equipment or wires.
- Remind students to wash their hands with soap and water after completing the lab.

Teaching the Lab

- Give students time to read through the lab and clarify any questions they might have.
- Suggest that students conduct a trial one time before gathering their data.
- Worms are delicate animals. Be sure they are handled gently. Rough handling can harm the worms and keep them from moving.
- Worms usually prefer moist soil and dark conditions.

Analyze and Conclude

1. Answers will vary. Students might look at dark v. light, warm v. cold, humid v. dry, soil v. sand, or a host of others. Accept all reasonable plans.
2. Answers will vary. Students might find that the worms tended to move toward one side of the pan or the other. Overall, students should report the worms prefer dark, moist, warm, or loamy soil conditions.
3. Answers will vary. Students should recognize that without proper moisture earthworms will dry up and die. Students might also recognize that with too much moisture, for example after a lot of rain, worms come to the surface. They must do that to maintain homeostatis because worms take in oxygen through their moist skin.
4. Answers will vary. For the sample procedures, the students should be able to identify factors such as light, temperature, or the shape of the pan as constants. It is important that the constants are maintained so that the results can be attributed only to the independent variable—in this case, moisture in the soil.
5. Answers will vary. Students might say that the lamp shone too brightly over the entire pan, and this was no longer a controlled variable.
6. Answers will vary, but students will probably find that worms preferred loamy soil, and warm and moist environments.

Write and Discuss

Answers will vary based on the environmental conditions studied. Students who hypothesized that the worms would prefer a dark environment over a light one should report that their hypothesis was correct.

Inquiry Extensions

1. Students might wish to investigate burrowing behavior. They could create two thin-walled containers, each one constructed by placing one cylinder inside a glass vessel of slightly larger diameter. Container 1 could have one type of soil, and Container 2 another type. Student observations should report on differences in time spent burrowing for set periods of time, and/or tracking the animal's castings.
2. Students might wish to study if seedlings are benefited or harmed by the presence of earthworms in the soil. An experimental design would have to include two identical sets of plantings, one with earthworms present and one without. Measurements on the number and height of healthy seedlings should prove whether or not the hypothesis was supported.

Lab 28 • Design Your Own
What is living in the leaf litter?

Objectives
- Observe organisms found in soil or leaf litter.
- Identify the organisms.

Process Skills
observe, classify, infer

Time Allotment
45 minutes on the first day
15 minutes for observations the following day

Materials

2-L clear plastic bottle	1/4-inch mesh wire screen (10-cm square)
scissors	
trowel	forceps
cheesecloth or plastic wrap	spoons
rubber bands	500–1000 mL soil sample
desk lamp	leaf litter
magnifying lens	pine cones
jars—one large, one small	identification guide

Possible Hypothesis
Arthropods are the most varied non-microbial life forms found in soil samples.

Possible Procedure
1. Cut a 2-L plastic bottle in half. Turn the top half upside down to serve as a funnel.
2. Place a small circle of wire screen in the mouth of the funnel. Do not pack it too tightly.
3. Place the funnel inside the large beaker.
4. Fill the funnel with soil and leaves.
5. Observe the soil, and make a qualitative assessment as to how wet or damp it is. Indicate your assessment in your data table.
6. Cover the sample with a piece of cheesecloth, and secure it with a rubber band.
7. Place the lamp over the cheesecloth, and turn it on.
8. Check back in 20 min.

9. Record your observations in the data table. Provide a detailed sketch of the animals that you see.
10. Clean up the materials as directed by your teacher.

Preparation
- Collect soil from a variety of sources, or identify places for students to gather their own samples.
- Have several identification guides available for student use.
- Remind students that none of the animals they find in this experiment should be handled.
- Students should wash their hands after handling soil or leaf litter.
- To avoid the danger of fire, keep the lightbulb a safe distance from the cheesecloth and the leaf litter.

Teaching the Lab
- Remind students not to disturb the funnel once it is placed in the beaker.
- Students will probably find that millipedes and other small animals are best observed with the use of a magnifying lens.
- Have students list the features of typical arthropods before beginning the lab. This will help focus their identification skills.
- The scarcity of organisms might be related to the season. Depending on your climate region, the best time of the year to do this lab might be in late spring or early fall.
- Students should find animals such as worms (which are not arthropods), centipedes, beetles, millipedes, and pill bugs.

Data and Observations
Sample data table

Organisms Observed in Soil Sample					
Detailed Sketch of Organisms	Number Found	Size	Unique Characteristics	Tentative Identification	Confirmed Identification
	1	4 mm, including legs	white and brown stripes on abdomen; brown cephalothorax	garden spider	*Salticus scenicus* zebra jumping spider

Note: number and type of organisms found will vary greatly with season, geographic location, and site from which sample is taken.

Teacher Guide and Answers, continued

Analyze and Conclude

1. The soil started out damp and clumpy. The heat from the lamp dried out the soil, and it became loose.

2. Answers will vary. Students might find centipedes, spiders, pill bugs, millipedes, and worms (which are not arthropods).

3. The animals moved away from the heat and the drying soil.

4. Most of the arthropods found in the leaf litter will use crawling as their primary means of locomotion. If the sample includes beetles or grasshoppers, they also have wings that they can use to cover broader areas.

5. Students will probably find that the biggest error was in identifying the organisms or in planning an effective method for making the animals visible.

6. Students might find that there were several ways to make the animals visible. They might find adding more water to the system might help to flush out the animals, rather than using heat to make them move.

Write and Discuss

Hypotheses that posited that arthropods would be present in the sample should have been supported by the data students collected. In their paragraphs, students should mention the variety and number of arthropods that were extracted from the leaf litter or soil sample.

Inquiry Extensions

1. Answers will vary. Students might mention larger animals, such as worms, snakes, or frogs that live in the area. Students will probably recognize that all the animals are part of a complex food web. Many of the arthropods in the soil transform leaf litter, shredding and consuming it, processing it for further decomposition by fungi and microbes.

2. Accept all reasonable experiments. Students should find that animals migrate deeper into the soil, below the frost line, or that they enter into a dormant phase.

Lab 29 • Classic

How can you analyze echinoderm relationships?

Objectives

- Examine samples of echinoderms and invertebrate chordates to determine characteristics.
- Create a cladogram to represent the evolutionary relationships among these animals.
- Make inferences about the significance of these relationships.

Process Skills

compare and contrast, analyze, classify, design

Time Allotment

45 minutes

Materials

diagrams
ruler
glue
paper
markers/colored pencils

specimens: sea star, brittle star, sea urchin, sea cucumber, feather star, sea squirt, and lancelet

Alternative Materials

- If you are unable to find enough examples of the organism for each group, substitute detailed photographs and drawings.

Preparation

- Assemble actual samples (live or dead) of the echinoderms and invertebrate chordates in this exercise for all students to see. If necessary, have students work on one animal at a time rather than on a complete set.
- Distribute a large sheet of paper, colored pencils, and rulers to each group.
- Photocopy pictures of these organisms so students can cut and paste them into their cladogram if their drawing skills are not adequate.
- Warn students that the samples are very fragile and should be handled with care.

Teaching the Lab

- Review the construction of cladograms with students with a simple example before starting the lab.

Teacher Guide and Answers, continued

• Make sure students are finding useful characteristics. Circulate around the room to help prevent any problems or answer questions that might arise.

• Assure students that there is more than one way to complete this cladogram. Their diagram might be different from another student's. It all depends on which characteristics they chose to study.

Data and Observations

1. Table 1

Echinoderm Characteristics							
Animal	Characteristic						
	Radial symmetry	Tube feet	Long arms	Leather-like skin	Nerve chord	Teeth-like structures	Spines
Sea squirt	−	−	−	+	+ (only in larval form)	−	−
Lancelet	−	−	−	+	+	−	−
Sea urchin	+	−	−	−	−	+	+
Sea cucumber	+	−	−	+	−	−	−
Sea star	+	+	+	−	−	−	−
Brittle star	+	+	+	−	−	−	−
Feather star	+	+	+	−	−	−	−

2. Sample cladogram

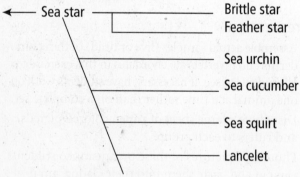

Analyze and Conclude

1. Answers will vary. Most students will probably list "invertebrate" as the primitive characteristic. This is not necessary to include as a derived characteristic because all of these animals share this characteristic.

2. Answers will vary, but students will probably mention characteristics such as spiny skin, arms,

tube feet, radial symmetry, teeth-like structures, and nerve chord. These would be among the best choices because these characteristics help differentiate the animals from one another.

3. These organisms move slowly and are often filter feeders.

4. Echinoderms do not have a nerve cord, while invertebrate chordates do.

5. Students might mention unfamiliarity with the echinoderm and invertebrate structures or features as a source of error.

6. Brittle stars are most closely related to sea stars. A sea squirt or lancelet is most distantly related. This is demonstrated by the fact that the sea squirt and lancelet share the fewest number of characteristics with the sea star. Sea urchins and sea cucumbers share at least one characteristic with sea stars.

Inquiry Extensions

1. Encourage students to use a variety of resources to find more information about echinoderms and invertebrate chordates. They might also want to look at early, extinct organisms to see how these animals have evolved over time.

2. Approve students' plans if they seem reasonable. Provide students with materials to create their models and show how these animals move or obtain food. Models will vary depending on the organism being studied.

Lab 30 • Classic
How have frogs adapted to land and aquatic habitats?

Objectives
• Observe a live frog.
• Compare and contrast a frog to humans.
• Identify useful adaptations of frogs.
• Research one adaptation.
• Make a model of the adaptation to share with the class.

Process Skills
observe, compare and contrast, identify, research, model

Time Allotment
45 minutes for the lab; allot another day for research and presentations

Materials

live frog
paper towels
tabletop
water

pencil with an
eraser
large aquarium

Alternative Materials

- Toads can be used in place of frogs.

Preparation

- Prepare a large aquarium tank for several frogs. Obtain the frogs from a local pond, a previous experiment, or from a pet store. If ordering from a science supply store, most will require two to three weeks for delivery.
- Frogs can be kept in a large plastic tub containing water and rocks.
- Remind students that the frog is a living creature that should be handled carefully with gentleness and respect.
- Instruct students to wash their hands with water and disinfectant soap after handling the frog.
- Disinfect the tabletops with a ten-percent bleach solution.
- Plan what to do with the frogs after the experiment. You might elect to keep them in an aquarium, or return them to the supply house, or return them to the wild if they were obtained from the wild.

Teaching the Lab

- Help students identify the parts of the frog by providing identification guides and textbooks for their use.
- Circulate around the room to ensure students are on task and finding the correct characteristics.

Data and Observations

Sample data table

Observation Data		
Trait	**Frog**	**Human**
Body shape/ length	trunk, head, four appendages/ about 20 mm	head, neck, trunk, four appendages / about 160 cm
Neck	no real neck	defined neck / about 10 cm
Eyes	bulging, on sides of head	on face, deep in sockets
Ears	external eardrums, no protection	internal eardrums, well protected

Observation Data, *Continued*		
Nostrils	two openings at front of the head	two openings at the front of the face
Skin	smooth, slightly cool and damp; can be spotted	smooth, slightly warm and dry; has hair follicles
Feet	webbed	not webbed
Length of hip to knee and knee to foot	about 76 mm	about 75 cm
Movement type/length of stride	jumps/ about 50 cm	walks upright/ about 125 cm
Breathing	breathes air with lungs and skin / about 120 respirations per minute	breathes air with lungs only / about 15 respirations per minute

Analyze and Conclude

1. Answers might vary. Both frogs and humans have four appendages. A human has a neck, head, and torso. Frogs have a head that is attached directly to the torso, with no neck. The frog and human both have bilateral symmetry.
2. Adult frogs breathe air through their lungs and also through their skin.
3. A frog has bulging eyes that sit atop its head while human eyes sit in recessed sockets in the skull. Both human and frog eyes have irises and pupils.
4. A frog has webbed feet, bulging eyes on the sides of its head, strong legs for jumping, sticky pads on its feet, and damp, smooth skin.
5. Answers will vary based on the adaptation the students explored. For example, students who chose to study skin secretions might have discovered that the frogs produce them for a variety of reasons, including oxygen exchange or toxicity against predators.
6. Answers will vary. Frogs' legs show an advantage for colonization of land; in particular the long jump allows frogs to elude certain predators.
7. Answers will vary. Students might find that their frog is too scared to cooperate.

Inquiry Extensions

1. Students might choose to observe salamanders, newts, or toads. A student who selected salamanders would notice similarities to frogs in that they both have smooth skin, bulging eyes, and four limbs. Dissimilarities include the presence of a tail and lack of webbing between the toes.

2. Answers will vary. Many species of salamanders and newts produce highly toxic skin secretions; brightly colored skin markings serve as a warning to predators.

Lab 31 • Classic
What are the structures and functions of a chicken egg?

Objectives
- Identify the different parts of a chicken egg.
- Recognize how substances can pass across a membrane during osmosis.
- Infer how the egg is suited to existing on land, as opposed to in the water.

Process Skills
examine, identify, infer, conclude

Time Allotment
45 minutes on the first day
10 minutes per day for the next four days

Materials
petri dish
tweezers
magnifying lens
metric ruler
2 unfertilized raw
  chicken eggs (the
  larger the better)
hard-boiled chicken
  egg (the larger the
  better)
paper towels

small plastic knife
microscope
microscope slide
cover slip
distilled water
clear corn syrup
vinegar
clear plastic cup
balance
rubber gloves
aluminum foil

Preparation
- Hard-boil enough eggs for each group before the laboratory starts.

Teaching the Lab
- Review proper use of a microscope and how to make a wet-mount slide with students prior to beginning the lab.
- Explain to students that cells use their membranes to regulate the amount of water and other substances that are inside the cell. The membranes of the egg work the same way.

- Remind students not to eat anything given to them in a laboratory setting.
- Have students wash their hands after handling the raw eggs.

Data and Observations
Sample Table 1

Comparison of Egg Structures					
	Shell	Yolk	Albumen	Membranes	Chalaza
Hard-boiled egg	brittle	firm, yellow with green outline and white center	firm and white	tough	no longer present
Raw egg	porous	yellow, viscous	gooey liquid, clear to whitish in color	tough	thick, white, cord-like structure

Sample Table 2

Osmosis in Shelled Egg						
Liquid	Amount of Liquid		Mass of Egg		Egg Observations	
	Before	After	Before	After	Before	After
Vinegar	150 mL	Answers will vary, but value will be less than 150 mL.	Answers will vary.	Answers will vary but will be more than before.	looks like a normal egg	shell gone, egg increase in size
Corn syrup	150 mL	Answers will vary, but value will be more than 150 mL.	Answers will vary.	Answers will vary but will be less than before.	shell-less, shriveled egg	egg will shrink
Distilled water	150 mL	Answers will vary, but value will be less than 150 mL.	Answers will vary.	Answers will vary but will be more than before.	shell-less, shriveled egg	egg will bloat

Analyze and Conclude
1. An eggshell is porous, but it is not permeable to water. Air can pass through, however. The shell of a hard-boiled egg seems to be more brittle but tougher.
2. The yolk provides the nutrients the chicken needs, just like a placenta in a mammal.
3. The eggshell dissolved and gained liquid when it was put in the vinegar. The vinegar dissolved the shell and moved across the membrane to enter the egg.

4. There was a higher concentration of water inside the egg than in the syrup solution, so water left the egg to enter the syrup. This caused the egg to shrivel.

5. The egg now had less water than the surrounding environment. Water moved from the beaker into the egg, causing it to increase in size again.

6. Breaking the egg's contents at any time is a cause for error. In addition, incorrect measurement of mass would be an error.

7. The bird eggshell is not permeable to water; this is one adaptation to life on land. Amphibian eggs are permeable to water and depend, at times, on nutrients carried across the membranes by water.

Inquiry Extensions

1. *Ovoviviparous* refers to organisms whose fertilized eggs develop within the body of the mother until they hatch or just before. Each embryo depends on its egg's yolk sac, however, not a placenta, as occurs with *viviparous* organisms, such as mammals. Animals that make use of this method include most sharks, some salamanders, and two toad species. An advantage to this method is that more young benefit from the physical protection of the mother, ensuring a larger number of viable offspring (eggs or hatchlings are not as readily preyed upon). Also, nourishment derived from maternal secretions in the oviduct ensures stronger young that can seek their own food sooner.

2. Different dinosaurs had different behaviors surrounding their eggs. Encourage students to choose two different dinosaurs to use in their comparison.

Lab 32 • Design Your Own
What is the best way to keep warm?

Objectives
- Form a hypothesis comparing the insulating properties of wet wool socks and dry wool socks.
- Design an experiment to test the hypothesis.
- Compare the temperature of water in the socks over time.

Process Skills
control variables, make comparisons

Time Allotment
45 minutes

Materials
wool socks (1 pair)	room-temperature
1-L glass beaker	water
plastic containers	stopwatch
with lids (yogurt	scissors
containers, 250 mL) (3)	craft knife
thermometers	rubber bands
(non-mercury) (3)	graph paper
hot tap water	colored pencils

Possible Hypothesis
When wool becomes wet, it will not have the insulating power that it did when it was dry.

Possible Procedure
1. Place one empty yogurt container in a dry wool sock.

2. Wet the other wool sock with room-temperature water, and place the second yogurt container into the sock.

3. Place the third container on the lab table to use as a control.

4. Carefully cut an *X* in the three tops.

5. Carefully pour the same amount of hot water into each of the three yogurt containers. Fill them nearly to the top.

6. Place the lid on each container, and insert a thermometer through the *X* in the lid.

7. For each container inside a sock, gather the sock around the thermometer and secure with a rubber band to ensure that the container is completely covered.

8. Measure the temperature immediately and record in your data table. Take the temperature readings every 5 min for at least 15 min.

Preparation
- Make sure each group uses containers of identical shape and size.

- Keep a large container of hot water available for the students to use to make sure they are all using water at the same temperature. It should be kept at 40–45°C. A coffee maker is a great source of quick hot water and is relatively inexpensive.

- Remind students to use caution when pouring hot water.

- Students should walk slowly when carrying beakers of hot water.
- Students need to use caution when making an *X* in the lid and when handling the craft knife.
- Students need to use caution if using glass thermometers.

Teaching the Lab
- Introduce the experiment with a discussion on the use of insulation in a variety of scenarios.
- The containers should cool in the following order: no sock, wet sock, dry sock.
- At the conclusion of the lab, be sure students understand that the wool does not generate heat but traps heat. Many students have the preconception that sweaters and coats produce heat, when in fact they just hold in body heat. The same is true for animal coats.

Data and Observations
Sample data table

Warmth Data				
Container	Temp. at 0 Min	Temp. at 5 Min	Temp. at 10 Min	Temp. at 15 Min
No sock	45°C	36°C	29°C	25°C
Wet sock	47°C	44°C	39°C	36°C
Dry sock	46°C	44°C	41°C	38°C

2. Graphs will vary, but students should see the most dramatic change in temperature with no sock, then the wet sock, and the least change in temperature with the dry sock.

Analyze and Conclude
1. Exact temperatures will vary, but the most extreme changes will be in the container with no sock. There will be some changes in the wet sock setup and little change for the dry sock.
2. The container with no sock was the control. It showed how the temperature would change in an un-insulated cup.
3. Mammals such as sheep and some goats produce thick wool to guard their skin against extremes in temperature. Other mammals, such as horses, deer, and cows, are covered with fur, but the fur does not provide as much insulation as thick wool.

4. Answers may vary. Students should recognize that their timing and measurements of temperature are possible places for error. Also, students might have failed to control all variables other than the independent variable. For example, initial temperature of all containers should be the same, volume of H_2O in all containers should be the same, and size and shape of all containers should be the same. If any factors such as these are varied, any results achieved might not be due to manipulation of independent variables, and therefore are possible sources of error.
5. Wet wool will keep one's feet warmer than wearing no socks at all.
6. Answers may vary, but most groups should get similar results.

Write and Discuss
Answers will vary depending on the original hypothesis agreed on by each group. Students should have found some difference in insulating ability between the wet wool and the dry wool, but they both work better than nothing.

Inquiry Extensions
1. The setup might be the same. Students might choose to use a cotton T-shirt. They might expect that there would be a big difference between the insulating abilities of wet and dry cotton.
2. Answers will vary. Blubber found in animals that live in and around water would compare to layers of fur for animals that live on land.

Lab 33 • Classic
How do we learn?

Objectives
- Conduct an experiment to answer questions about human learning.
- Make predictions about learning and performance.
- Communicate your findings in an appropriate manner.

Process Skills
pose questions, make predictions, conduct experiments, collect and graph data

Time Allotment
45 minutes

Materials
pencil or marker
maze puzzle (12 copies)
  [See How to Use the Student Models, pp. T24–T31.]
portable CD or MP3 player with earphones
music or voice recording
stopwatch

Alternative Uses of the Lab
- If your school has a sociology or psychology class, this lab might present a good opportunity for a cross-curricular activity.

Preparation
- Make 12 photocopies of the lab for each pair of students.

Teaching the Lab
- Help students with their mirror setups.

Data and Observations
Sample Table 1

Data for Trial 1	
Trial	Results With Mirror
1	2 min, 38 s
2	2 min, 26 s
3	2 min, 10 s
4	2 min, 15 s
5	2 min, 08 s
6	2 min, 00 s

Sample Table 2

Data for Trial 2	
Trial	Results Without Mirror
7	2 min, 30 s
8	2 min, 20 s
9	2 min, 08 s
10	2 min, 12 s
11	2 min, 04 s
12	1 min, 58 s

Analyze and Conclude
1. Answers will vary. Students might predict that performance will continue to improve so that trial 12 will show the fastest time of all. Advanced learners might predict that each change in the conditions will slow down the completion time.
2. Answers will vary. Students might report that even though the addition of the stressor and the change of visual cues caused a temporary delay, the overall trend was toward a faster completion of the task.
3. Answers will vary. Students might report that the subject continued to improve on time despite the stressor. This might give that person an advantage in noisy learning environments.
4. Answers will vary. Students should conclude that the ability to learn new behaviors despite the presence of stressors would be an advantage to an animal in its environment, where there are many distractions.
5. Answers will vary. Students might report that their time-taking was inaccurate. Students might also report that learning (or mastery) of the skill decreased the completion time, whereas fatigue might have increased the completion time.
6. Answers will vary. Students should find that data from other groups will follow the same trend of performance improvement and then level off.
7. Answers will vary. Student line graphs for the completed trials should show an *S*-pattern that levels out as the extra trials are repeated. For lines showing a prediction, students should realize that once a best time is achieved, it is hard to improve on it. The line should flatten out as trials continue.

Inquiry Extensions
1. You might want to encourage students to do this for homework and have them repeat the task again after 1, 4, and 6 hours.
2. Encourage students to choose simple songs everyone knows, like "Row, Row, Row Your Boat," "Twinkle, Twinkle Little Star," or "Jingle Bells."

Lab 34 • Classic
How long can you last?

Objectives
- Assemble a muscle-testing device based on directions and diagrams.
- Test the muscle fatigue experienced after repetitive motion over a period of one minute.
- Serve as a counter and recorder as other group members test muscle fatigue.
- Draw conclusions about muscle fatigue.

Process Skills
design models, make apparatuses, conduct experiments, observe, draw conclusions

Time Allotment
45 minutes

Materials
rubber bulb
1/2-inch plastic or vinyl hose, 1 m in length
1/2-inch PVC pipe, 20 cm in length
ring stand
test tube clamp
paper flag, 2.5 cm square; red on one side, white on the other
stopwatch
cellophane tape
duct tape
first aid tape

Alternative Materials
- rubber pipette bulb

Preparation
- You might want to assemble the muscle-testing devices before the class starts. This could cut down on confusion and ensure there is enough time for all students to conduct the experiment.

Teaching the Lab
- Ensure that students have attached the flags so that they can move but still settle back to their original position. The best way to do this might be with a thin piece of tape.
- To prevent the bulb from falling off of the tester's elbow or the back of the knee, use first aid tape to secure the bulb and hose.
- Make sure students are completely squeezing the bulb. Circulate around the room to ensure they are using the proper method.

Data and Observations
Sample data table

Fatigue Data		Number of Squeezes	Number of Red Flags	Comments
Tester 1	Hand	12	11	hand felt tired
	Arm	20	20	arm getting tired, but not as tired as hand
	Leg	26	26	not tired
Tester 2	Hand	12	11	hand started to cramp
	Arm	20	20	arm is tired
	Leg	26	25	not tired
Tester 3	Hand	28	27	hand felt tired
	Arm	20	20	arm got tired
	Leg	26	26	thigh is burning

Analyze and Conclude
1. The hand squeezed, the upper arm and the lower arm worked together to squeeze the ball, and the thigh and calf muscles worked to squeeze the ball behind the knee.
2. Sample answer: Muscle fatigue occurs when muscles become tired from use. Often the muscles do not work as well if they are fatigued, and they might not be as strong as they are when they are fresh. This experiment was an exercise in fatigue. The same motion was repeated over a minute and the effects of fatigue were reported by the Tester.
3. Answers will vary. Some students might find that squeezing the ball in their hand was the most fatiguing; other students might have found that the leg muscles fatigued the quickest.
4. Answers will vary. Students who run a lot might report that their leg muscles were the strongest, while students who play guitar or type a lot might have found that their hand muscles were strongest.
5. Students might recognize that error could have been introduced if they did not squeeze the bulb completely or if they tried to increase the number of squeezes at the expense of raising the flag.
6. Student answers will vary. Students might notice that physically active students might have stronger arms and legs, while more musically or computer-inclined students might have stronger hands.

Laboratory Manual

Inquiry Extensions

1. Answers will vary. Students might find that they are less likely to become fatigued as quickly if given the opportunity to rest between trials.

2. Answers will vary. Students might notice their muscles fatiguing more quickly with each successive trial. Some students might report that the isometric test is much less difficult than the repetitive-action test. Depending on the experimental design, students might find the continuous contractions require a longer trial before muscle fatigue sets in.

Lab 35 • Design Your Own
How quickly do you respond?

Objectives

- Form a hypothesis about the effect that one variable, such as time of day, has on reaction time.
- Design an experiment to test the effect of your variable on hand and foot reaction times.
- Compare the results of reaction times with and without the variable.

Process Skills

develop hypotheses, control variables, draw conclusions

Time Allotment

45 minutes

Materials

stopwatch
cover of frying pan (for the steering wheel)
small blocks of wood (for brake and gas pedals) (2)
rubber ball
rubber mat

Alternative Materials

- You can substitute a toy steering wheel for the frying pan cover or another appropriate disklike object.

Possible Hypothesis

Eye-to-hand and eye-to-foot reaction times are better in the morning hours and worse in the afternoon. [Students might select other test variables such as increased heart rate and respiration, dizziness, or poor vision (using sunglasses or glasses with an incorrect prescription for the subject).]

Possible Procedure

1. Set up a model of a car. Use the frying pan cover as the steering wheel. Label one block of wood *brake* and another block of wood *gas*. Set up the cover and the blocks as they would appear in a real car. Place a rubber mat beneath the blocks of wood to prevent them from slipping.

2. Choose a time in the morning to test reaction times.

3. Working in groups of four, take turns with your lab partners to run the test and collect the data.

4. Have one person in your group act as the timer and one person as the recorder. The third person will create the diversion, while the fourth person will be the driver.

5. Sit the driver down at your "car." Tell the driver that you are going to test the reaction time of his or her hands and feet. Explain that he or she will pretend to drive and a ball will fly in front of the windshield. You will observe how quickly the driver moves the steering wheel and moves his or her foot from the gas pedal to the brake.

6. Test the reaction time of his or her hands first. The person creating the diversion will stand to the side of the driver and throw the ball so it passes in front of his or her field of vision. The timer should stand directly behind the driver and see how long it takes for the driver to respond.

7. Repeat the procedure, but this time observe how long it takes for the driver to move his or her foot from the gas to the brake.

8. Repeat steps 5–7 for the other students in your group.

9. Choose a time of day in the afternoon, and conduct the experiment again on each of the drivers.

Preparation

- Have supplies available the students might need to perform their experiments. If you do not have the materials they are looking for, help them modify what is available.
- Caution students not to throw any objects directly at the test subject.
- Use caution when selecting frying pan covers. Some metal covers are sharp and can cut the skin. Glass covers can drop and shatter.

Teaching the Lab

- You might want the students to perform their experiments in a larger area, such as the gymnasium or outside. This will limit interference among the other experiments.
- You might choose to act as a traffic signal; holding up green, yellow, or red flags will help simulate driving conditions.

Data and Observations

Sample data table

Driver Reaction Times				
Driver		Hand Reaction	Foot Reaction	Comments
1	8 A.M.	0.4 s	1.0 s	
	4 P.M.	0.6 s	1.5 s	
2	8 A.M.	1.0 s	0.8 s	
	4 P.M.	1.5 s	1.0 s	
3	8 A.M.	1.0 s	2.0 s	
	4 P.M.	2.0 s	4.0 s	
4	8 A.M.	1.0 s	2.0 s	
	4 P.M.	2.0 s	4.0 s	

Analyze and Conclude

1. Answers will vary. The sample data show that the reaction times became longer in the afternoon.
2. Answers will vary. The sample data indicate that the best time for a teenager to drive is in the morning because their reactions are quicker.
3. Students might find that it takes longer for the feet to react than for the hands.
4. The control is the reaction time without the stimulus.
5. Answers will vary. Students might indicate that timing the beginning of the reaction was difficult.
6. Answers will vary. Some students might find that early morning is not a good time for reaction times.

Write and Discuss

In this example, the data supported the hypothesis that reaction times were shorter in the morning than in the afternoon. Students might remark on the difficulty of capturing accurate times.

Inquiry Extensions

1. Challenge students to do some research on this issue and then compare their results. Recent studies have shown that a driver using any cell phone, whether hand-held or hands-free, is four times more likely to be involved in an accident.
2. Students' responses will vary. Simple stimuli might include smelling food, a bell ringing to signal class change, or temperature changes. Positive stressors might include sports/exercise, parties, exciting films, or video games. Negative stressors might include homework or tests, arguments, running to catch a bus, or missing a friend. Graphs can show all responses for the period of data collection, with a line rising and falling with the intensity of the stimulus, or students might elect to graph events separately, providing greater detail for each event. Higher-level students might use two lines in each graph, one for the action of the stimulus, and the second for the response.

Lab 36 • Design Your Own
How much air can your lungs hold?

Objectives
- Identify a factor that influences lung capacity.
- Design an experiment to test that factor.
- Draw conclusions about what impacts lung capacity.

Process Skills
identify factors, design experiments, draw conclusions

Time Allotment
45 minutes; first part indoors, second part outdoors

Materials
round balloons (12-inch maximum diameter)
thermometer (non-mercury)
measuring tape
string
metric ruler
calculator

Possible Hypothesis
The lungs can take in more air on a warm day than on a cold day.

Teacher Guide and Answers, continued

Possible Procedure

1. While inside the classroom, stretch a balloon several times. Take a deep breath, and blow into the balloon. Exhale as much air as possible. Capture the air of one exhalation only.
2. When finished, tightly hold the end of the balloon so that no air escapes.
3. Use a measuring tape to measure the balloon's circumference, or have your lab partner place a string around the largest section of the balloon.
4. Use a ruler to measure the length of the string in centimeters, and place this value in the data table.
5. Repeat steps 1–4 three more times, and record the results in your data table.
6. Change the value of the circumference of the balloon to cubic centimeters using the following formulas where C is the circumference of the balloon and d is the diameter. For these calculations, students can use 3.1415 for the value of pi (π).
    $C = \pi \times d$
    $d = C/\pi$
    volume: $1/6 \times \pi \times d^3$
7. Repeat steps 1–6 four times outside on a cold day. Record your data in the data table.

Preparation

- It would be best to conduct the outdoor part of the experiment on a day when the air temperature is 15.5° C or colder.
- To maintain the balloons' elasticity, make sure that students keep their balloons close to their bodies when they go outside.
- Make certain that students do not share balloons.
- If you have students who have lung conditions such as asthma, make certain that they do not over-exert themselves.
- Make sure the students use a new balloon before each series of tests.

Teaching the Lab

- Provide students with the following information:
  - Write the conversion formulation on the board.
  - Total Lung Capacity (TLC) for an average adult male is about 5000 cm³.
  - TLC for an average adult female is about 4000 cm³.

- Total Lung Capacity comprises four measurements:

Abbreviation	Measurement	Description
VE	tidal volume	volume inhaled
IRV	inspiratory reserve volume	maximum inhaled volume after a quiet exhalation
ERV	expiratory reserve volume	maximum exhaled volume after a quiet exhalation
RV	residual volume	volume of air in the lungs after maximal exhalation

- If the students' balloons are not round, push on the outside to achieve a more round shape.

Data and Observations
Sample data table

Volume of Air Exhaled			
Trial	Temperature	Balloon Circumference (cm)	Exhalation Volume (cm³)
1	22.2° C	23.4	216.3
2	22.2° C	23.9	230.5
3	22.2° C	23.3	213.6
4	22.2° C	23.2	210.8
Average	22.2° C	23.45	217.76
1	1.6° C	22.5	192.3
2	1.6° C	21.3	163.1
3	1.6° C	18.9	114.0
4	1.6° C	21.8	174.9
Average	1.6° C	21.13	159.31

Analyze and Conclude

1. A person's lung capacity might tell how physically fit they are, how they might endure athletic activity, or how they might handle cold weather.
2. Answers will vary. Students will probably have found a concrete example for their hypothesis and will have learned that lung capacity increases in warm weather.
3. Answers will vary. Students might find that students with asthma have a lower lung capacity. Athletes or musicians might have a greater lung capacity.

4. Answers will vary. Students might suggest using a transparent bottle with a small balloon inside and a larger balloon stretched over the bottom. They could then model the lungs by pushing on the stretched balloon.

5. Answers will vary, but students might cite problems with weather conditions in their experiment. In addition, the balloon's elasticity, or lack thereof, can also affect the results.

6. Answers will vary depending on which factors the other groups studied.

Write and Discuss

In this example, the data supported the hypothesis that the lungs are able to exhale more warm air than cold air. Students who compare data with their peers might be surprised at the variance in exhalation volume.

Inquiry Extensions

1. Students might find that smokers have the lowest lung capacity. Most nonsmokers will have a higher lung capacity. The most telling variable will be the lung capacity of those who live with smokers. The survey should also ask these people if they play sports, have asthma, or play a wind instrument. Comparing lung capacity data against the results of the survey will help students draw final conclusions.

2. Students might predict that smog and altitude can decrease lung capacity. One thing that they might do is create a survey to give to people in different parts of the country to see how these conditions impact people's lives. Students who study diseases that affect lung capacity will likely find data on asthma, bronchitis, emphysema, or chronic obstructive pulmonary disease. Workers whose workplaces pose risks to lung health include miners, toxic-waste workers, fire fighters, artists, and metalworkers, among others. Students can review statistics from the federal Departments of Labor or Health and Human Services to further their research.

Lab 37 • Classic
How healthy are they?

Objectives
- Test urine samples for the presence of glucose using glucose test strips.
- Test urine samples for the presence of protein using Biuret solution.
- Create a data table.
- Interpret test results.

Process Skills
observe, interpret data

Time Allotment
45 minutes

Materials
test tubes (6)	Biuret solution
test-tube rack	simulated urine
plastic droppers (6)	samples (3)
water	wax pencil
glucose solution	white paper or
protein solution	paper towels
glucose test strips (6)	

Preparation
- Prepare the glucose solution by dissolving 10 mL 10% glucose solution in 990 mL of water.
- Prepare the protein solution by dissolving 10 g of albumin or pepsin in 990 mL of water. (Pepsin is preferred because albumin will make the sample cloudy; this might tip off some students as to which is the protein-enhanced sample.)
- Add a few drops of yellow food coloring to make the solutions the same color as urine.
- Transfer enough of each solution to beakers marked Patient 1, Patient 2, and Patient 3 respectively so that there is enough for students to take appropriately-sized samples. Assign the protein-treated solution to Patient 1. Assign the untreated water to Patient 2. Assign the glucose-treated solution to Patient 3.
- Biological supply companies are good sources of glucose test strips and Biuret solution. Review with students the MSDS for hazardous material. [See Preparation of Solutions, pp. T13–T15, on the use of Biuret solution.]

- Mixing a solution of 50-percent glucose solution and 50-percent protein solution would denote a patient who is positive for both protein and glucose. A fourth patient can be added to the test, if time permits.

Teaching the Lab

- Encourage students to label the droppers and to always return them to the proper test tube. This will avoid contamination.
- Glucose test strips will turn green in the presence of glucose.
- Biuret solutions will turn purple-pink in the presence of protein.

Data and Observations
Sample data table

Simulated Urine Sample Data			
Test For	**Water**	**Glucose**	**Protein**
Glucose	yellow	green*	yellow
Protein	light blue	light blue	purple
Test For	**Patient 1**	**Patient 2**	**Patient 3**
Glucose	negative	negative	positive
Protein	positive	negative	negative

* Note: Color for positive results might differ with the brand of test strip. Please refer to packaging.

Analyze and Conclude

1. The changes in color show a positive test for glucose.
2. The changes in color show a positive test for kidney disease. Patient 1 tests positive for protein in the urine.
3. The sample from Patient 2 will show no reaction on the test strip or with the Biuret solution. It is the normal sample.
4. The patient who tested positive for glucose (Patient 3) needs to be tested further for diabetes. The positive test shows glucose in the urine, a symptom of diabetes.
5. The patient who tested positive for protein (Patient 1) should be tested further for kidney disease. The positive test shows protein in the urine which is a symptom of kidney disease.
6. Answers will vary, but students may mention cross-contamination in their answer.

7. Doctors should do further testing. A single test does not provide enough evidence. Family history should be explored and more tests undertaken.

Inquiry Extensions

1. Students might suggest that people eat food with less sugar or carbohydrates. Urine can be monitored to see how glucose levels are impacted by diet and meal time. Students might also suggest that exercise will impact glucose levels.
2. Urine samples are used to test for pregnancy, or the presence of certain vitamins, chloride, or illegal drugs, among other things.

Lab 38 • Design Your Own
How do you digest protein?

Objectives
- Design an experiment.
- Compare conditions for the function of pepsin in the digestive process.
- Collect and interpret data, and draw conclusions about the conditions within the stomach.

Process Skills
design an experiment, interpret data, draw conclusions, control variables, compare

Time Allotment
45 minutes one day
15 minutes the next day

Materials
test-tube rack
2% pepsin solution
blue litmus paper
boiled egg white
  or firm tofu
plastic knife
ruler
graduated
  cylinder
test tubes with
  stoppers
marking pencil
2% hydrochloric
  acid solution
stirring rod (glass)

Possible Hypothesis
Hydrochloric acid and pepsin are needed to digest protein in the stomach.

Possible Procedure

1. Check the egg cubes with a ruler for uniformity of size. Use a plastic knife to trim cubes that are too large.

2. Label four test tubes *1, 2, 3,* and *4,* and place them in the test-tube rack.

3. Add three cubes of egg to each test tube. Record the general appearance of each of the cubes in your data table.

4. Add 10 mL of pepsin to test tube 1. Record any immediate reaction the enzyme has with the egg in your data table. If there is no reaction, write *no reaction.*

5. Add 5 mL of pepsin to test tube 2. Then add 5 mL of water to that test tube. Observe any immediate reactions and record in the data table.

6. Add 5 mL of hydrochloric acid and 5 mL of water to test tube 3. Observe and record any immediate reaction with the egg.

7. Add 5 mL of pepsin to test tube 4. Then add 5 mL of hydrochloric acid. Observe any immediate reaction, and record this information in the data table.

8. Dip a clean stirring rod into the solution in each test tube. Then touch the stirring rod to a strip of blue litmus paper. Observe any reaction that occurs. Record this in your data table.

9. Insert stoppers into the test tubes, and follow your teacher's instructions about where to place them.

10. The following day, record any observations about the condition of the egg whites. Repeat step 8 for all the test tubes.

11. Dispose of the test materials as instructed by the teacher. Wash your hands thoroughly with soap and water.

Preparation

- Prepare a 2-percent solution of hydrochloric acid and a 2-percent pepsin solution. [See Preparation of Solutions, pp. T13–T15.]

- Boil eggs and cut the whites (or cut the tofu) into 0.5-cm cubes. Prepare enough for students to have three cubes per test tube.

- Remind students that hydrochloric acid is corrosive, can cause chemical burns, and should be handled with caution.

Teaching the Lab

- Suggest to the students that they make clear, concise descriptions of the protein cubes, using terms such as "firm," "sharp edges," and "white."

- If necessary, review the litmus-test procedure and possible results with the students.

- Discuss ways to prevent cross-contamination of the test tubes by using a clean stirring rod for each litmus test and by using clean graduated cylinders when adding new fluids to each test tube.

- If student's results are not evident, the egg cubes might be too big or the hydrochloric acid solution might be too weak.

Data and Observations

Sample data table

Digestion Process Test				
Test Tube	Egg-White Appearance		Litmus Color	
	Day 1	Day 2	Day 1	Day 2
1	no reaction	no change	no change	no change
2	no reaction	no change	no change	no change
3	no reaction	no change	red	red
4	egg bubbles	beginning to dissolve	red	red

Analyze and Conclude

1. Pepsin and hydrochloric acid combined digest the egg white best. After one day, the solid egg white in test tube 4 began to dissolve. The egg whites in the other test tubes were undissolved.

2. The reaction did not occur immediately, so it was not a fast reaction. Students should recognize that they cannot determine exactly how long it took.

3. In a controlled experiment, it is important to keep all the variables the same except for one. In this way, one is assured that the variable that is being manipulated is responsible for any change.

4. Pepsin alone or with water will not digest protein. It works best with a low pH, as provided by the hydrochloric acid, for digestion to occur.

5. Students might find that one source of error was in measuring the liquids. Another source of error could be that egg pieces of different sizes would have reacted at different rates because different amounts of surface area were exposed.

6. The control was test tube 1, with just pepsin. Since we knew that pepsin was an enzyme, any reaction in this tube would show that pepsin could digest protein on its own without the presence of HCl.

7. Answers will vary. All students should find that pepsin needs hydrochloric acid to begin the digestive reaction.

Write and Discuss

Students should report that pepsin worked better in the presence of hydrochloric acid. They might also report that the failure of HCl alone to digest the protein was interesting.

Inquiry Extensions

1. Students should learn that small pieces of protein are digested faster than large pieces because more surface area is exposed to the enzymes and other digestive juices. Chewing food aids this process by breaking morsels into smaller pieces.

2. Answers will vary depending on the experimental design. Adding more food will slow the digestive process. Adding more pepsin and HCl will make it occur more quickly. Students can study the effects of temperature on the reaction and find that it will occur faster at higher temperatures. If the temperature is too high, the pepsin will degrade and slow digestion.

Lab 39 • Classic
How does a body grow?

Objectives

- Compare the average height of humans with the average length of body parts during various stages of human development.
- Graph the average height of humans.
- Analyze rates of human development, male or female, based on the data assembled and graphed.

Process Skills

organize information, interpret data, design experiments

Time Allotment

45 minutes

Materials

metric ruler   calculator
graph paper   colored pencils

Preparation

- Provide students with illustrations from magazines of people of varying ages.
- Encourage students to compare the images and describe the general differences and similarities between these people.
- If necessary, remind students how to calculate percentages.
- Remind students that the figures used in this exercise are median heights.

Teaching the Lab

- Make sure students understand how to read the graph before they begin their investigation.
- Students should recognize that the models in **Figure 1** are of identical size to assist in comparing proportions.
- Students might have trouble estimating between the lines. Circulate through the room to troubleshoot any problems that might arise.
- Allow students to use calculators to make their mathematics easier.

Data and Observations

Sample data for Table 1

Proportions of Body Parts to Total Height		Newborn	Five Years	Fifteen Years	Adult
Size of head compared to length of body	female	23%	19%	16%	14%
	male	23%	19%	16%	14%
Size of torso compared to length of body	female	35%	28%	25%	23%
	male	35%	30%	28%	30%
Length of legs compared with length of body	female	47%	51%	53%	58%
	male	47%	51%	53%	53%

Note: Answers will vary. Percentages might differ slightly based on points of measurement and rounding off.

Analyze and Conclude

1. The proportion of the head to total body length decreases, while the proportion of the torso to total body length increases.

2. The rate of change in proportion is greater during the early years of development. Some change in proportion occurs throughout the growth process.

3. Answers will vary. Students might answer that the graph provided visual confirmation of the dramatic changes in proportion in early development and subsequent reduction in rate of change in later development.

4. Proportions related to the head would be expected to decrease, while proportions related to the torso and limbs would be expected to increase.

5. Students should feel confident that they could reach such a conclusion, based on the information they have already collected and graphed.

6. Students should feel confident that they could make a reasonable estimate based on the information they have collected and graphed.

7. Answers will vary; possible answers include mismeasurements, mistakes in the graph, or faulty calculation of proportions.

Inquiry Extensions

1. The ratios change slightly. The world's tallest man (250 cm) has these proportions: legs 50 percent of total height, torso 35 percent of total height, and head 15 percent of total height.

2. Answers will vary. Students should find that their proportions are most similar to the median measurements for the 15-year-old of the appropriate gender.

Lab 40 • Classic
Who needs a banana peel?

Objectives

- Prepare and observe bananas over a period of five days.
- Model the skin's defense against disease using banana peels.
- Conduct an experiment controlling variables.
- Form a conclusion about the necessity of washing and cleaning cuts to prevent disease.

Process Skills

make models, control variables, draw conclusions

Time Allotment

45 minutes the first day
10 minutes per day over the next 5 days

Materials

sealable plastic bags (4)	water
	paper towel
fresh bananas (4)	toothpick
rotten banana	cotton swab
permanent marker	rubbing alcohol

Alternative Materials

- This lab can work with any fruit that has a skin, such as an apple or an orange.
- Plastic knives can be used in place of the toothpicks.

Preparation

- Provide a rotten banana as a source of bacteria. For the most distinct results, be sure to use bananas that are rotten, not merely over-ripe. One rotten banana can be used by four to five lab groups.
- Remind students not to taste anything in this experiment.
- Students should wash their hands with soap and water when they have finished handling the fruit.
- Review the MSDS for rubbing alcohol.
- Remind students not to open the bags. The molds and bacteria could be allergenic or pathogenic.

Teaching the Lab

- Caution students not to pierce the peel of the banana while washing it and preparing for the experiment.
- Make sure that students do not pierce the banana peel when scratching it with the toothpick in step 6.
- Students should dip the toothpick into the rotten banana each time they touch the experimental banana.
- Remind students that the humidity in the room can influence how fast a banana ripens, and be sure they keep careful track of their control banana.
- If digital cameras are available, students can use them to document the changes in the bananas.

Data and Observations

Sample data for Table 1

Banana Observation Data				
Day	Banana 1 (no contact with rotting fruit)	Banana 2 (contact with rotting fruit, peel intact)	Banana 3 (contact with rotting fruit, peel pierced)	Banana 4 (contact with rotting fruit, peel pierced, treated)
1	no change	no change	slightly dark near scratch site	no change
2	no change	no change	scratched areas soft and dark	slightly dark
3	no change	no change	very soft and dark	becoming soft
4	soft and darkening uniformly	soft and darkening uniformly	becoming liquidy	soft and dark
5	soft and darkening uniformly	soft and darkening uniformly	a mess	soft and dark

Analyze and Conclude

1. The rotten banana was the source of pathogens. It represented an infected individual.

2. Bananas 1 and 2 were very similar in color and firmness. Banana 3 showed the most decay. Banana 4 was similar to Bananas 1 and 2 in color and firmness; the scratches had only mild discoloration.

3. Banana 1 was the control. Its color changed from yellow with green to yellow with brown spots. Its tissue went from being very firm, to slightly less firm, to even less firm with soft spots in certain areas.

4. Students might report that they touched the wrong fruit with the infected toothpick; they failed to cover all of the scratches with alcohol, or did not cover the entire length of the scratch; or that they failed to close the bags securely.

5. Like the banana peel, the skin is a physical barrier between pathogens in the outer environment and the warm, moist environment inside the body. Pathogens that get past the barrier cause rapid deterioration of the more vulnerable tissues. Rubbing alcohol is an antiseptic that kills microorganisms. In this experiment, the alcohol killed many of the bacteria that were transferred to the cut banana peel, thus limiting the decay.

6. Yes; if a barrier is broken, applying a cleansing agent can help prevent a serious infection.

Inquiry Extensions

1. Students might elect to repeat the test using a bar of plain soap and an antibacterial soap to see if antibacterial soap really kills germs better than plain soap and water, or they might change the source of the bacteria to another fruit or vegetable or even an animal source.

2. Students should be able to demonstrate the chain of transmission between infected items and non-infected items.